THE FLIGHT OF
THUNDERBOLTS

Oxford University Press, Amen House, London E.C. 4

GLASGOW NEW YORK TORONTO MELBOURNE WELLINGTON
BOMBAY CALCUTTA MADRAS CAPE TOWN

Geoffrey Cumberlege, Publisher to the University

THE FLIGHT OF THUNDERBOLTS

BY

B. F. J. SCHONLAND, F.R.S.

OXFORD
AT THE CLARENDON PRESS
1950

PRINTED IN GREAT BRITAIN

But to him who's scientific
There is nothing that's terrific
In the falling of a flight of thunderbolts;
Yes, in spite of all my meekness,
If I have a little weakness
It's a passion for a flight of thunderbolts.

GILBERT AND SULLIVAN
The Mikado

To my friends who shared the weakness

JAMES CRAIB

D. J. MALAN	D. B. HODGES	H. COLLENS
J. S. ELDER	J. A. KEILLER	E. C. HALLIDAY
	BERNARD PRICE	

PREFACE

IN writing this book I have tried to keep in mind those readers who are interested in the general development of science as well as those who have a particular concern with lightning and lightning-protection. The subject, in its progress from myth to knowledge, provides a 'case-history' of general interest and a good illustration of the scientific method in action.

The book is not a detailed monograph, and the more complicated aspects of the problem have been touched upon rather lightly. I have had to omit, or to summarize very briefly, the contributions of many leading scientific men, including some, like C. T. R. Wilson, G. C. Simpson, E. V. Appleton, and R. A. Watson-Watt, to whose work my own owes a great deal.

I should like to thank Professor I. Schapera of the University of Cape Town for supplying me with information on the lightning beliefs of the Bantu, and Mr. C. J. Monk and Mr. D. G. Kingwill for helpful comments and information. I wish to thank the staff of the Clarendon Press for their helpfulness during the preparation and printing of this book.

B. F. J. S.

THE BERNARD PRICE INSTITUTE FOR
   GEOPHYSICAL RESEARCH,
UNIVERSITY OF THE WITWATERSRAND,
JOHANNESBURG

1 *July* 1949

CONTENTS

LIST OF PLATES

1

BEFORE THE LIGHTNING-ROD

Thunder Magic

'Deo tonanti; Deo fulminatori!'; 'Tonnerre!'; 'Donner-wetter!'; 'Umpundulo!'; 'What in the name of thunder?'

MAN has always had a wholesome respect for the destructive power of the lightning-flash, and his age-old fear of lightning is shown by the extent to which what is called 'thunder magic' enters into the religions and folk-lore of primitive peoples. The words describing thunder and lightning remain to this day mildly sacrilegious oaths in many languages, and the name of Jove is still invoked; our primitive ancestors believed that the terrible and unpredictable power of the thunderbolt lay in the hands of divine powers.

To the Norsemen, lightning was caused by the magic hammer, Mjollner, of their fierce red-headed god Thor, who hurled it to the earth from a goat-drawn chariot rolling thunderously upon the anvil-topped clouds of heaven. As evidence for their belief, broken pieces of the hammer-head, either iron or stone of a kind not usual in the neighbourhood, were often found buried in the soil. Countrymen who turn them up with the plough call them thunder-stones to this day, but more prosaic names for them are meteorites and stone-age implements.

Amongst most of the Bantu tribes who form the black races of southern Africa, as once amongst the North American Indians, the belief is general that lightning is produced by a magical thunder-bird, Umpundulo, which dives from the clouds to earth and whose vivid plumage and beating wings give rise to the flash and to the thunder. As visible signs of the thunder-bird's passage the Basutos and the Barotses point to the marks of its claws on the scarified bark of damaged trees and on the poles of huts struck by lightning.

A number of beautifully carved soapstone statues of a bird

resembling an enormous hawk have been found in the great ruined temple of Zimbabwe in Southern Rhodesia. As many archaeologists consider that Zimbabwe was built by a ruling Bantu race which has long since vanished, and as no other graven image has been found in it, one may venture the suggestion that it was the temple of the thunder-bird.

The bird known as the thunder-bird varies in type from tribe to tribe, being often a seahawk or a spur-winged goose, rare visitors to inland areas. When it can be caught by a witch-doctor its fat and bones are used to produce magic medicine with which to protect dwellings and to frighten other thunder-birds away. If, in spite of his efforts, lightning strikes a hut which has been anointed with this medicine, the witch-doctor usually explains that the owner had failed to pay for the necessary renewal.

Persons struck by lightning, if they survive, are regarded as unclean, and have to go through elaborate purification ceremonies. Those killed are buried immediately, without ceremony or mourning, for they have incurred the wrath of the Great Spirit. Animals destroyed by lightning are never eaten, however hungry the people may be. If a tree is struck it is still the custom in the less civilized tribes for a search to be made for the eggs or droppings of the thunder-bird, which may hatch out later into more such unwelcome visitors. Such a tree is avoided by passers-by and is not cut for firewood lest evil befall the user.

The witch-doctors of many Bantu tribes are charged with the duty of driving storms away, particularly if they threaten the kraal of the chief. This they do by challenging the thunder-birds with loud shouts and by blowing warnings on flutes made from the bones of thunder-birds which they claim to have killed. In some tribes the witch-doctors are credited with the power to direct the birds to dive on the huts of their enemies, and are thought to be able to turn themselves into thunder-birds for this wicked purpose. According to the Roman historian, Pliny, the Etruscan priests were believed to have similar directive powers.

Between 1926 and 1930 three accusations against witch-doctors concerning crimes of this kind, which involved the control of lightning as a guided missile, were brought before the native courts of the Kgatla tribe in the Bechuanaland Protectorate. One was a charge of actual murder by lightning; the accused pleaded guilty and admitted that he had success-fully directed a lightning-flash to kill another man. The other two cases were charges of malicious damage to property, both of the accused having set huts alight by directed lightning. All were found guilty and punished; the confessed lightning murderer (to make the punishment fit the crime) was, by order of the presiding chief, severely branded in the mouth with a piece of burning wood.

In ancient Egypt it was the god Typhon (Seth) who hurled the thunderbolt, but whether from lack of recorded history or from the fact that thunderstorms are not so frequent on the Nile, there is no information available as to his methods or intentions.

Many early statues of Buddha show him carrying in his right hand a double-headed Vajra or Dorjē, a thunderbolt with prongs at each end, like a pointed dumb-bell. The chief temple of Sera, near Lhasa in Tibet, has a special reputation as the resting-place of a famous Dorjē, which the priest manipu-lates in various ways during prayer. The emblem is carried in solemn procession to the Jokhany, the great sanctuary, during the New Year Festival.

In Greece and Rome a lightning-flash was one of the chief indications of the displeasure of the father of the gods, Zeus in the case of Greece and Jupiter or Jove in that of Rome, and was often used by him to punish offending mortals with death or with damage to their property. Herodotus, the Greek historian, relates how Zeus, being highly offended at the Scythian emperor Scyles, who had demanded that the priests of Bacchus initiate him into the sacred mysteries of the temple of that god, threw a thunderbolt and destroyed the palace of the emperor. Zeus frequently intervened with thunderbolts when his favourites on earth were in danger of losing in battle.

Homer tells how, at the siege of Troy, 'Zeus himself thundered furiously from Mount Ida and sent his burning lightning against the Greeks; they, having seen it, were amazed, and pale fear seized them all'. In view of their subsequent success against the Trojans it would seem that the Greeks never really knew when they were beaten.

The thunderbolt was used not only by Zeus himself, it was available also to members of his family. The poet Virgil relates how the goddess Pallas Athene borrowed some of her father's 'rushing lightning' to transfix a very unpleasant and boastful Greek called Ajax on his return from the fall of Troy.

The prayers of the faithful could sometimes induce the gods to use their armoury upon their enemies. In this tradition the psalmist David called upon Jehovah to 'Cast forth thy lightning and scatter them; shoot out thine arrows and destroy them'.

Since the thunderbolt was considered the weapon of the gods, it was sacrilege to imitate its bright light or to mimic the sound of thunder. Virgil tells of the fate of one Prince Salmoneus, who wished to be called a god by his subjects and to receive divine honours from them, and for this purpose drove his chariot over a brazen bridge to show how he could make thunder, while torches hurled on either side demonstrated that he could produce lightning as well. For this impiety Zeus threw a real thunderbolt at him and burnt him up, after which he was placed in Hades near a better-known brother of his, Sisyphus.

In the Roman Empire the religious ritual of lightning became more highly developed than it had been with the Greeks. The laurel bush, which was sacred to Apollo, was considered, according to Pliny, to be immune from lightning. For this reason the Emperor Tiberius, who was 'immoderately afraid of thunder' though 'neglectful of religious matters', used to don a wreath of laurel during thunderstorms. An edict ascribed to King Numa (700 B.C.) forbade the eating of the flesh of animals killed by a lightning-stroke. Persons who had been killed by lightning were considered to have incurred the wrath of the gods and were buried hurriedly where they died. The spot was walled in and became a minor shrine dedicated to the god of thunder, for it was consecrated by Jupiter's sacred fire. Augustus Caesar erected an altar to Jupiter on the spot where he had had a narrow escape from being struck. Houses damaged by lightning were similarly consecrated and could under no circumstances be repaired or rebuilt. It is recorded that one Valerius Publicus had the audacity to rebuild his house on the Palatinate after it had been destroyed by a flash, and that the magistrates of Rome insisted that it be pulled down again.

It was believed that Jove used his thunderbolts not only as a punishment but also as a warning when he was dissatisfied with the way the Roman State was being run. His most serious recorded action was to destroy by lightning the gilded statue of Romulus, one of the founders of Rome, which stood upon the Capitoline Hill. This event, which occurred in the days of Cicero and Catiline, was naturally considered an extremely bad omen and a strong indication that the gods considered that all was not well with the government. In the same storm, possibly by the same flash, the bronze statue of the wolf-nurse of Romulus and Remus was struck and the hindlegs were melted. The damage can be seen by the curious to this day on the original statue, which is kept in the Capitoline Museum of Rome.

The Romans were a mixed race, with a high proportion of Etruscan blood and traditions which came to them from the north. To the Etruscan people, whose ancestors lived on the thundery slopes of the Alps, lightning was a more familiar event than to the southerners or the Greeks, for thunderstorms are much more frequent in northern Italy than anywhere else in Europe. The people of Venice and Genoa see at least three times as many storms each summer as those of Rome and Athens, and hear thunder near to them on more than twenty days each year. With the Etruscan traditions the Romans inherited the Etruscan belief in divination by lightning, which became part of the system of Roman statecraft and lasted for many centuries.

Divination is the science of finding out the wishes of the

gods by means of signs and portents in the sky. In Rome the practice of this science was entrusted to a very august body known as the College of Augurs, membership of which was bestowed upon persons of distinguished merit. It was held for life and, because of its political influence, was much sought after; for the augurs, by conveying the will of Jupiter, could veto decisions, meetings, and elections of the highest importance.

The College of Augurs consisted originally of three members, of whom the King was one. It was formed very early in Roman history, certainly as early as 300 B.C., and was in existence as late as the fourth century A.D. In the time of Julius Caesar it had sixteen members, who ranked in importance next to the members of the Pontifical College. The toga of an augur was striped with scarlet and edged with purple, and was perhaps the forerunner of the doctor's academic gown. In his hand the augur carried a staff of office with a curled-round top, not unlike a bishop's crozier.

An augur ascertained the feelings of the gods on matters of State by making observations of three auspicious objects which appear at random in the sky—lightning, birds, and shooting-stars. He always looked south while carrying out his duties, and if a lightning-flash was seen to pass from left to right it indicated a favourable omen for State affairs. If it passed from right to left the augur was bound to report that Jupiter did not approve of what was going on in the Forum or elsewhere. There was, however, more to it than this; the mere appearance of any lightning at all during the time of the augur's observation had to be reported to the magistrates of Rome, who would thereupon cancel the meetings of all public assemblies for the day.

The magistrates were legally bound to take appropriate action on an augur's report, but other observations of lightning made by persons who were not augurs were not considered by them. Since the taker of the auspices was constitutionally subject to no authority who could test the truth of his observations, the augurs' reports of lightning became in time a useful

political device to obtain postponement of unwanted meetings
of the Public Assembly and to cancel the results of elections to
which the elder statesmen objected. The practice was used,
often no doubt wisely, by the oligarchy of the Roman State
when it wished to delay the passage of laws or the election of
certain magistrates by popular assemblies. As time went on an
augur who intended to stop a measure would simply tell the
proposer beforehand, 'I will watch the sky'. Nobody supposed
that he really would make observations of lightning; it had
become accepted as a formula for announcing opposition, a
form of veto, and according to the real strength of the
contending parties the proposal was proceeded with or
dropped.

In 59 B.C. the consul and augur Bibulus held up the whole
legislative programme of Julius Caesar by 'watching the
heavens'. In the following year a law was passed to prevent
such obstructive tactics being applied again to the passage of
legislation, though it would seem that the augurs' power to
cancel elections remained. Whether this law was effective is
not certain, but in 45 B.C. all the methods of divination employed by the College came under the satirical criticism of
Cicero in his well-known essay on Divination. 'We regard
lightning on the left hand as a most favourable omen,' said he,
'for everything except an election. No doubt this exception
has been made to allow the rulers of the State to use political
expediency to decide the correctness of an election for magistrates, judges, or legislators.' An earlier and more fundamental
critic was the philosopher Lucretius (99 to 55 B.C.), who asked
why, if Jupiter sent the lightning, he should scatter his bolts
in so wasteful and unreasonable a fashion on the sea and on
his own temples, why he should show such a preference for
high mountains, forests, and trees, and why he had to wait until
thick clouds had formed before launching them.

In Greece there was no such extensive thunder-divination,
and it was not there raised to the Roman level of statecraft.
Once a year watchers on the walls of Athens waited in considerable excitement until they saw a lightning-flash from

Harma, which was accepted as a good omen for the setting out of the sacred procession to the shrine of Apollo Pythius at Delphi. For a favourable omen from lightning the Grecian diviner looked for a flash to his right, not as in the Roman case to his left, but as he faced north the east was in both cases the auspicious quarter.

The Early Record of Damage caused by Lightning

'From lightning and tempest, from plague, pestilence, and famine; from battle and murder and from sudden death: Good Lord, deliver us.'

From the earliest times, when man lived in huts which had to be placed on hill-tops to give him sight of approaching enemies and to keep away the wild animals of the wooded valleys, lightning was an act of God for which there was no real remedy but prayer. In Europe, including England, it was, however, for many centuries the general practice to supplement prayer by the violent ringing of church bells. Whenever a thunderstorm was imminent the bell-ringers were called to their churches to ring peals. 'The poor believed that this pious exercise dispersed the evil spirits of the storm, whilst the better sort said that it caused some kind of undulation in the air and broke the continuity of the lightning path.' For this reason the inscription 'Fulgura Frango' ('I break up the lightning-flashes') is often to be found on medieval bells. The practice of bell-ringing in thunderstorms was, however, extremely dangerous to the ringers, and in 1786 the Parlement of Paris found it necessary to reissue an edict, said to have been first promulgated by Charlemagne and repeated in later years, to make the custom illegal on account of the many deaths it caused to those pulling the ropes. How necessary this edict was can be judged from figures given in a book published in Munich in 1784 with the cautious title, *A proof that the ringing of bells during thunderstorms may be more dangerous than useful*. The author, Fischer, stated that in 33 years lightning had struck 386 church towers and killed 103 bell-ringers at the ropes. These figures are not surprising when the accounts of lightning striking and damaging church steeples and other elevated structures are examined, for such damage was very frequent.

Perhaps the most famous of these structures is the Campanile of St. Mark in Venice. This has had a very bad lightning history. It stands over 340 feet high in an area which, as already mentioned, experiences many thunderstorms. It was severely damaged by a stroke in 1388, at which time it was a wooden structure. In 1417 it was set on fire by lightning and destroyed. In 1489 it was again reduced to ashes. In 1548, 1565, and 1653 it was damaged more or less severely, and in 1745 a stroke of lightning practically ruined the whole tower. Repairs cost 8,000 ducats (£3,000 in those days), but in 1761 and 1762 it was again severely damaged. In 1766 a Franklin rod was installed on it and no further trouble from lightning has occurred since.

The record of damage to churches, whose elevated steeples attract the lightning-flash, is voluminous. The beautiful cathedral tower of Siena was repeatedly struck and damaged until the year 1777, when a lightning-rod was installed. The innovation was much against the wishes of the Siennese, who called it a heretic rod until it had shown its protective value. The old church of St. Paul's in London was twice severely damaged before Wren's present cathedral took its place.

On Wednesday, the fourth of June, 1561 . . . the steeple of Paule's in London, being fired by lightning, brast forth (as it seemed to the beholders) two or three yards beneath the foote of the crosse and from thence burnt down the speere to the stone worke and bels, so terribly that in the space of four houres the same steeple with the roofes of the church were consumed.

Wren's masterpiece was never seriously damaged by lightning, for a reason which will be given later, but the beautiful spire of St. Martin's-in-the-Fields was less fortunate. On 28 July 1842 this spire, which ninety years after Franklin's discovery was still not equipped with a lightning-rod, was struck by a flash which passed down the iron rod supporting the weather vane, jumped to the masonry of the spire and dislodged several blocks of stone, two of which fell into the church. It then passed down to the dials of the clock, through these to the metal frame of the bells, and finally to the lead roof of the main church building, from which it reached the ground through the drain-pipes. The spire was left in a very bad state and had to be completely rebuilt.

Similar damage was done in 1764 to the spire of another London church, St. Bride's, 85 feet of which had to be rebuilt. The Dutch church in New York was badly damaged in the same way in 1750 and 1763, and ceased to be in danger only after a lightning-conductor was fitted in 1765.

On the night of 14 April 1718, thunderstorms covered the coast of Brittany between Landerneau and St. Pol de Leon and damaged no less than twenty-four church towers. In 1774 a severe storm over London did considerable damage to St. Peter's Church besides striking a ship, two houses, and an obelisk in St. George's Fields, Southwark. On 11 January 1815, twelve church towers between the North Sea and the Rhenish provinces were severely damaged. On 25 April 1760, the abbey of Notre Dame at Ham, in France, was struck three times in twenty minutes and burnt to the ground.

With the development of artillery in the eighteenth century came the need to store large quantities of gunpowder in vaults and magazines. Churches had long been used as centres for the storage of weapons and food in time of war and their vaults and crypts were ideally suited for use as improvised powder magazines. The combination of tall steeples and explosive contents made them, however, very dangerous places during thunderstorms. It is not surprising that a number of disasters occurred from lightning striking the steeples and igniting the powder below.

The first recorded case was in 1769, when a flash struck the tower of the church of St. Nazaire in Brescia, in the vaults of which were stored 100 tons of gunpowder. The resulting explosion destroyed one-sixth of the city and caused the deaths of three thousand people. As late as 1856 at least four thousand people were killed as a result of the explosion of a large store of powder in the vaults of the church of St. Jean on the Island of Rhodes, the steeple having been struck by lightning. Similar explosions were the result of lightning-strokes to military powder magazines in Tangiers (1785), Luxemburg (1815), Venice (1808), and Navarino (1829). In 1782 a lightning-discharge set off 400 barrels of gunpowder at Fort Malaga in Sumatra, from which the lightning-conductors had been removed by order of the Council of the East India Company because they had been advised that lightning-rods were a danger and not a protection.

These are only a few of the most outstanding cases in the long record of lightning damage to churches and buildings. It is noteworthy, however, that there are many historic buildings which have never been seriously damaged by lightning because they have been protected by a form of lightning-conductor accidentally introduced into their construction. Of these the best known was the Temple of Solomon in Jerusalem, which, according to the orientalist Michaelis (1783, in correspondence with Lichtenburg), experienced no damage from lightning over a period of ten centuries. Accounts of the building describe it as having been covered inside and out with burnished plates of metal. The historian Josephus refers to them as gold, but the metal was probably only gilded. The gilded dome of the building was similarly covered, and bristled with long, pointed iron spikes, possibly to prevent birds (or thieves) from settling on it. Iron cisterns below the courts of the temple received the rain from the roof through iron pipes. A more complete system of lightning protection could hardly have been devised. When we consider how carefully the ancients recorded instances of damage to their public buildings by lightning, the silence of historians indicates that the temple of Jerusalem was actually perfectly protected against it.

A second structure which, in spite of much damage to churches round about it, has never suffered from lightning is the monument erected in 1677 in commemoration of the Great Fire of London. It has accidentally incorporated in its structure a most effective lightning-conductor, formed by the metal vase at the top, which is surrounded by pointed metal plates representing flames of fire. This is fixed to iron bars supporting iron steps, and the iron railing of these steps reaches to the bottom of the building. Though 202 feet high, the monument has never been damaged by lightning.

Another interesting case is that of the cathedral of Geneva. This is the most prominent building in the city and has a central tower built of wood. It enjoyed complete immunity from lightning for three centuries before it was fitted with a lightning-rod, though the neighbouring and much lower bell-tower of the church of St. Gervais was frequently struck and damaged. The immunity of the cathedral was investigated in 1771 by de Saussure, who reported that the wooden tower was completely covered with tinned iron plate, linked to the ground and to the metal in the structure.

There are many such examples of structures with roofs and domes covered with lead and other metals which have enjoyed similar immunity over centuries. Some of the most magnificent buildings of the Romans, including the Temples of the Capitoline Jupiter, of Venus, of Vesta, and of Rome itself, the Pantheon, and the forum of Trajan, were roofed with tiles of thickly gilded bronze which must have acted in some measure as lightning-conductors. The tiles from the first two temples were taken by Pope Honorius I (A.D. 625–38) to cover the basilica of St. Peter, whence they were stolen by the Saracens during the invasion of Rome in A.D. 846.

The roofs of the chief churches and palaces of Europe were covered in medieval times with lead and copper in large sheets. The beautiful wooden lantern tower of Ely Cathedral, like that of the cathedral of Geneva, has been saved for six centuries by its leaden roof, for it must have been struck many times. The same protection saved St. Paul's Cathedral from serious damage, before it was fitted with a conductor in 1769.

Until the time of Benjamin Franklin there is no record of any scientific explanation of the immunity enjoyed by these metal-roofed buildings, in spite of the extensive damage suffered by others not so roofed, particularly church steeples.

In 1773 Franklin pointed out that 'buildings that have their
roofs covered with lead or other metal, and spouts of metal
continued from the roof into the ground are never hurt by
lightning; as whenever it falls on such a building, it passes in
the metals and not in the walls.'

Damage to shipping

The masts of a ship at sea are an obvious target for a lightning-flash, and the old wooden-masted ships were particularly
liable to destruction or damage by lightning. Some idea of
the perils to which such ships were exposed when they ran
into thunderstorms can be gained from information collected
by Sir William Snow Harris in the early part of the nineteenth
century as ammunition for the long battle he fought with the
Admiralty to have the British Navy equipped with lightning-
conductors. From the official journals of H.M. ships he showed
that in sixteen years, from 1799 to 1815, there were 150 cases
of lightning damage to naval vessels. Nearly 100 lower masts
of line-of-battle ships and frigates were destroyed; one ship in
eight was set on fire in some part of the rigging or sails; about
70 seamen were killed and more than 130 wounded from this
cause. In ten cases the ships were completely disabled and com-
pelled to leave their stations at critical periods in the Napo-
leonic wars. The cost in material alone was estimated at
£100,000, a sum worth considerably more 150 years ago than
it is to-day. In addition to this damage several ships were lost
with all hands in violent thunderstorms, and one at least, the
Resistance, of 44 guns, was known from a survivor's report to
have been blown up by a lightning-flash in 1798.

Harris gives some interesting extracts from the ships' logs.
Captain Briggs, R.N., of H.M. Frigate *Clorinde*, off the coast
of Ceylon in 1813, wrote:

> About three in the afternoon we observed a dark cloud approach-
> ing from the windward quarter; this induced me to clew up the top-
> sails. About an hour later, the ship was struck by lightning. . . .
> The mainmast was shivered in pieces; only a wreck remained.
> Three men were killed and many hurt.

Captain Haydon, R.N., of H.M.S. *Cambrian*, off Plymouth on 22 February 1799, wrote:

Observed a tremendous squall coming down upon us; turned the hands up to clew up the close-rigged topsails. While they were so employed a ball of fire struck the topmast-head, killed two men and wounded many others. The number taken below amounted to about twenty.

In 1838, H.M.S. *Rodney*, 'one of the finest of our line-of-battle ships' was struck by lightning off the south-east coast of Sicily. The discharge destroyed the top-gallant mast, entered the lower mast and left it 'in a tottering state'; for the expansive effect was so great that thirteen of the iron hoops round the mast were burst open.

Apart from these and similar instances of damage to vessels of the Royal Navy there is, so far as the author knows, no collected account of the effect of lightning on wooden ships before they were protected either by the installation of conductors or, later, by the introduction of steel masts and hulls. From the earliest recorded times, however, lightning was a recognized and serious hazard to wooden shipping.

2

THE INVENTION OF THE LIGHTNING-ROD
BY BENJAMIN FRANKLIN

'Eripuit coelo fulmen sceptrumque tyrannis'—TURGOT
AFTER MANILIUS. (He snatched the lightning from the sky
and the sceptre from tyrants.)

IN the year 1600, William Gilbert, physician to Queen Eliza-
beth, made the first scientific study of electricity, and gave to
substances like amber and glass, which attracted light bodies
when rubbed, the name of 'electrics', from the Greek word
'electron', meaning amber. For 150 years afterwards the subject was very slowly developed and though various natural
philosophers, including Sir Isaac Newton, paid some attention
to it, the most noteworthy progress was in the construction of
the first frictional electrical machines. These were cylinders or
spheres of glass or sulphur mounted on an axle and rotated by
hand so as to rub against pads of leather (see Plate 1).

In 1746, Benjamin Franklin, successful master-printer, publisher, and citizen of Philadelphia, had reached the age of 40
and the period of comparative leisure for philosophical thought
and experiment to which he had long looked forward. In that
year he purchased some pieces of simple electrical apparatus
from a Dr. Spence, who had brought them with him from
Scotland, and settled down to making experiments with them
and with others of his own construction. It was a good year to
start, for in January 1746 Pieter van Muschenbrock of Leyden had made the important invention of the Leyden phial or
jar, a bottle with conducting coatings of tinfoil inside and out,
separated by the insulating glass. This was the first electrical con-
denser; in it electricity could be stored or 'condensed' for some
time. Its invention marked a great advance in the study of the
'electric fluid', and with it and the electrical machine Franklin
and his group of friends made outstanding contributions

to the science of electricity. Franklin determined the real nature of the condensing properties of the jar and it is to him, for the names arose naturally out of his important one-fluid theory of electricity, that we owe the terms 'positive' and 'negative' which are still applied to electrical phenomena. His most famous researches were, however, concerned with the manner in which sharp points of metal could remove or discharge the electricity from electrified bodies. From them he developed the principle of the metal comb which is in use to-day in many industrial applications of high-voltage electricity. It was from the study of the electric discharge from points that he was led to the conception of the lightning-conductor.

With frictional electrical machines, turned by hand like a grindstone, it was possible to make electric sparks a few inches long. Franklin's own electrical machine is now in the museum of the Franklin Institute of Philadelphia, and a photograph of it is reproduced as Plate I. A great many workers with these machines, including Newton, had commented on the similarity between short electric sparks and the lightning discharge. Franklin made the same observation and listed twelve points of similarity, including '9.—Destroying animals', for he not only killed a turkey with great ceremony at a picnic by the electric shock, but nearly killed himself on another occasion. To this list he added 'The electric fluid is attracted by points. We do not know whether this property is in lightning. But since they agree in all particulars wherein we can already compare them, is it not probable that they agree likewise in this? *Let the experiment be made.*' So was he the first to proceed from speculation on this matter to experiment and to attempt to test directly whether 'clouds that contain lightning are electrified or not'.

The method by which this question might be settled was described by him in 1750 in a letter to the Royal Society in these words:

On the top of some high tower or steeple place a kind of sentry box . . . big enough to contain a man and an electrical stand (an insulating glass stool). From the middle of the stand let an iron rod

PLATE I

Franklin's Electrical Machine
(*By courtesy of the Franklin Institute of Philadelphia*)

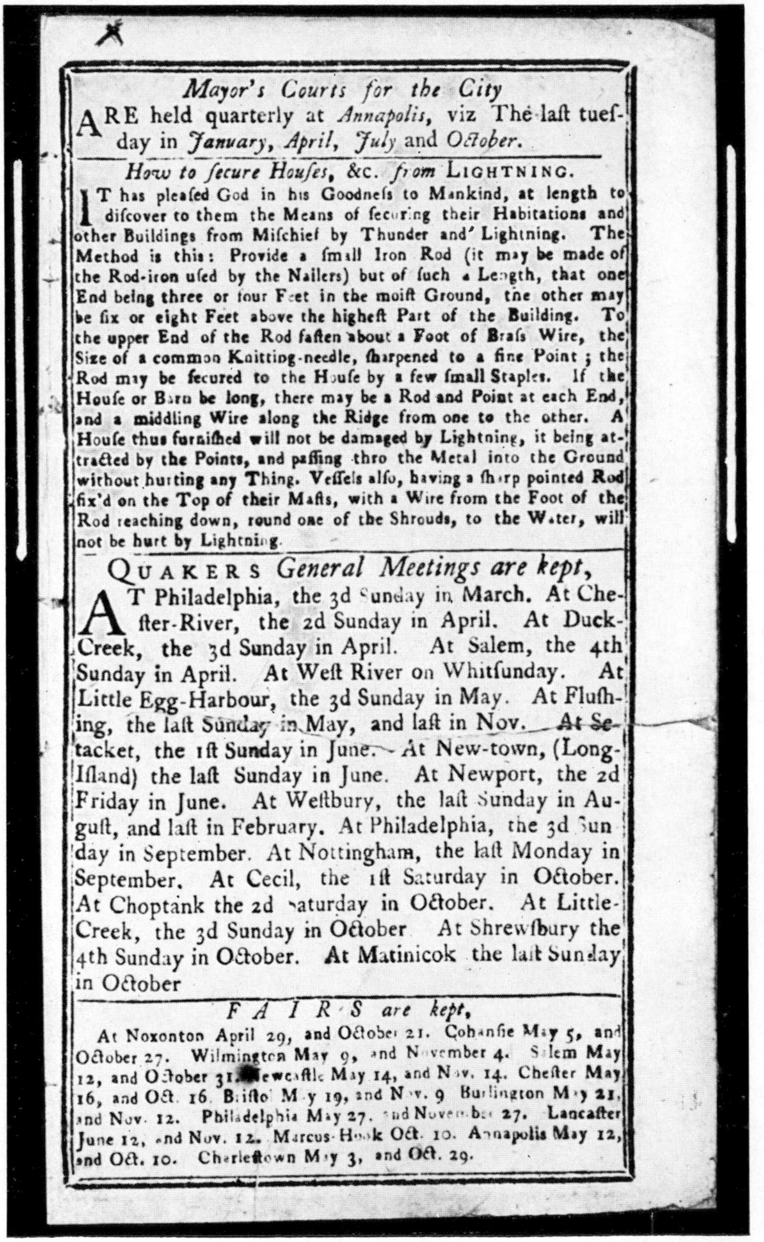

PLATE II

Mayor's Courts for the City

ARE held quarterly at *Annapolis*, viz The laft tuef-day in *January*, *April*, *July* and *October*.

How to fecure Houfes, &c. from LIGHTNING.

IT has pleafed God in his Goodnefs to Mankind, at length to difcover to them the Means of fecuring their Habitations and other Buildings from Mifchief by Thunder and Lightning. The Method is this: Provide a fmall Iron Rod (it may be made of the Rod-iron ufed by the Nailers) but of fuch a Length, that one End being three or four Feet in the moift Ground, the other may be fix or eight Feet above the higheft Part of the Building. To the upper End of the Rod faften about a Foot of Brafs Wire, the Size of a common Knitting-needle, fharpened to a fine Point; the Rod may be fecured to the Houfe by a few fmall Staples. If the Houfe or Barn be long, there may be a Rod and Point at each End, and a middling Wire along the Ridge from one to the other. A Houfe thus furnifhed will not be damaged by Lightning, it being at-tracted by the Points, and paffing thro the Metal into the Ground without hurting any Thing. Veffels alfo, having a fharp pointed Rod fix'd on the Top of their Mafts, with a Wire from the Foot of the Rod reaching down, round one of the Shrouds, to the Water, will not be hurt by Lightning.

QUAKERS General Meetings are kept,

AT Philadelphia, the 3d Sunday in March. At Che-fter-River, the 2d Sunday in April. At Duck-Creek, the 3d Sunday in April. At Salem, the 4th Sunday in April. At Weft River on Whitfunday. At Little Egg-Harbour, the 3d Sunday in May. At Flufh-ing, the laft Sunday in May, and laft in Nov. At Se-tacket, the 1ft Sunday in June. At New-town, (Long-Ifland) the laft Sunday in June. At Newport, the 2d Friday in June. At Weftbury, the laft Sunday in Au-guft, and laft in February. At Philadelphia, the 3d Sun-day in September. At Nottingham, the laft Monday in September. At Cecil, the 1ft Saturday in October. At Choptank the 2d Saturday in October. At Little-Creek, the 3d Sunday in October At Shrewfbury the 4th Sunday in October. At Matinicok the laft Sunday in October

FAIRS are kept.

At Noxonton April 29, and October 21. Cohanfie May 5, and October 27. Wilmington May 9, and November 4. Salem May 12, and October 31. Newcaftle May 14, and Nov. 14. Chefter May 16, and Oct. 16. Briftol May 19, and Nov. 9 Burlington May 21, and Nov. 12. Philadelphia May 27, and November 27. Lancafter June 12, and Nov. 12. Marcus-Hook Oct. 10. Annapolis May 12, and Oct. 10. Charleftown May 3, and Oct. 29.

The first public announcement of the lightning-rod in 'Poor Richard's Almanac' *for 1753*

(*Reproduced by courtesy of the Franklin Institute of Philadelphia*)

rise and pass bending out of the door and then upright twenty or thirty feet, pointed very sharp at the end. If the electrical stand be kept clean and dry, a man standing on it when such clouds are passing low might be electrified and afford sparks, the rod drawing fire to him from a cloud. If any danger to the man should be apprehended (though I think there would be none), let him stand on the floor of his box and now and then bring near to the rod the loop of a wire that has one end fastened to the leads (earthed roof), he holding it by a wax handle; so the sparks, if the rod is electrified, will strike from the rod to the wire and not affect him.

What Franklin had in mind in proposing this experiment is explained in the following paragraphs.

When an electrified body, such as a thundercloud, is near an insulated piece of metal, such as Franklin's iron rod, it draws a charge of opposite sign to the near end of the originally uncharged conductor and repels a charge of the same sign to the far end, as shown in Fig. 1. This is 'electric induction'. If the electric tension is sufficiently strong, some of the charge on the upper end of the rod will stream off it as a faint glow-discharge, and pass upwards to neutralize some of the charge on the bottom of the cloud. The electricity in this glow-discharge is carried upwards on molecules of the gases in the air, which in the case illustrated are charged positively and attracted by the negatively charged base of the cloud; such charged molecules are called ions, and their formation and their behaviour are further discussed in Chapter 5. In small-scale laboratory experiments like those carried out by Franklin the glow-discharge effect is much enhanced by fitting the rod with a sharp point. The process goes on until the rod has acquired a considerable excess of charge *of the same sign as that on the base of the cloud*. Franklin's experiment does not draw electricity from the cloud but has the same effect as if it had done so.

If the rod is not insulated but connected to the earth at its base, as in Fig. 2, the repelled negative 'induced' charge is no longer on the rod (having been repelled to a great distance) and the rod will discharge positive electricity so long as the cloud is near enough.

At the time this experiment was proposed there was no very high steeple in Philadelphia; the tower of Christ Church was being built, and Franklin could not carry out the experiment

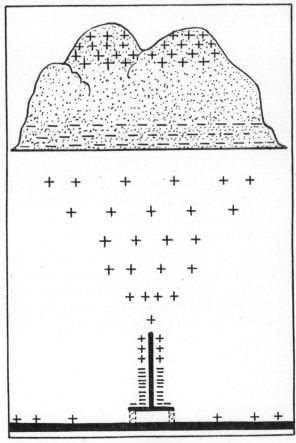

FIG. 1

immediately. His proposals were not considered important in England, but in France, where all the 'Philadelphian experiments' had excited great interest, the French physicist, d'Alibard, encouraged by Buffon, the great naturalist, determined to try out Franklin's idea without any tower at all. His iron rod was 40 feet long and he used a glass bottle to insulate it at its base, and wooden masts, to which it was tied with silk ribbon, to support it. The equipment was placed in the charge of an old soldier called Coiffier who, on 10 May 1752, at Marly,

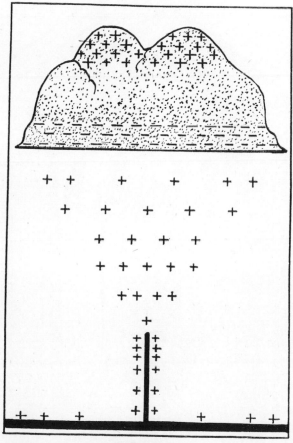

FIG. 2

near Paris, brought an earthed wire near to the rod while a thunderstorm was overhead and obtained the expected stream of sparks. He rushed to call the parish priest, who, followed by the amazed villagers, was witness to the first direct proof that thunderclouds were electrified.

The success of the experiment, which is illustrated in Fig. 3,

Fig. 3

was made widely known; very soon afterwards it was repeated in Paris and London. Franklin, before he himself knew anything about it, was acclaimed in Europe as a modern Prometheus who had shown how to draw the electric fire from heaven.

In default of the high tower which he had thought essential and without knowing of the success of the French experiment, Franklin meanwhile had decided to try it with a kite. No precise description of this historic episode was ever given by him, but Joseph Priestley, the great chemist, who got the story from him, tells it as follows:

Preparing, therefore, a large silk handkerchief and two cross-sticks of a proper length on which to extend it, he took the opportunity of the first approaching thunderstorm. . . . The kite being raised, a considerable time elapsed before there was any appearance of it being electrified . . . at length, just as he was beginning to despair of his contrivance, he observed some loose threads of the hempen string to stand erect and to avoid one another, just as if they had been suspended on a common conductor. (The string ended in an insulating silk ribbon.) Struck with this promising appearance, he immediately presented his knuckle to the key (hung on the string) and, let the reader judge of the exquisite pleasure he must have felt at that moment, the discovery was complete. He perceived a very evident electric spark. . . . This happened in June, 1752, a month after the electricians in France had verified the same theory, but before he had heard of anything they had done.

Franklin was no vague amateur; he saw clearly that the next interesting thing would be to find out the sign of the electric charge on the cloud above him. By September 1752 he had erected an iron rod on the chimney of his house in Philadelphia, connected by an insulated wire which ran down the stair-well to an iron water-pump, where it was earthed. Inside the house, 'opposite my chamber-door, the wire was divided; the ends separated about six inches, a little bell on each end and between the bells a little brass ball, suspended by a silk thread, to play between and strike the bells when clouds passed with electricity in them'. This device was the electric chimes invented by him in that year, and in this case it served 'to give notice when the rod should be electrified'. He provided himself with a Leyden jar to collect and store some of the charge on the rod, another jar which he could charge with electricity of known sign from a rubbed glass rod, and finally an electroscope, a testing device consisting of a cork ball hung from a silk thread, to indicate the sign of the charge collected from the rod by comparing it with that in his second Leyden jar.

His own account of his first trial is:

At last, on April 12th, 1753, there being a small gust (storm) of some continuance, I charged one phial pretty well with lightning and the other equally as far as I could judge with (positive) electricity from my glass globe (by rubbing it with silk). Having placed them properly, I beheld with great surprise and pleasure, the cork ball fly briskly between them and was convinced that one bottle (the lightning bottle) was electrified negatively. I repeated this several times and in eight succeeding gusts and concluded that the clouds are always electrified negatively. On June 6th I met with one cloud that was electrified positively, though several that passed over my rod before, during the same gust, were in the negative state. . . . (I conclude that) *the clouds of a thundergust are most commonly in a negative state of electricity, but sometimes in a positive state—the latter, I believe, is rare.*

Franklin's 'great surprise and pleasure' at the successful result was well justified. It was a beautifully planned experiment, arrived at after several years of thinking about the problem, including, no doubt, the dangers attached to the investigation, and it gave a definite answer to the question as to the sign of the charge on the base of a thunder-cloud. The statement in italics above remained the only direct and reliable information on this question for 170 years. After much modern discussion and elaborate experiment it could not be put in better words to-day, except that for 'clouds' we would now substitute 'bases of clouds'.

But Franklin's ingenious and practical mind was already ahead of his experiment. In the same year (1750) in which he proposed this trial of thunderstorm electricity, he wrote for the first time of the lightning-rod:

May not the knowledge of this power of points be of use to mankind in preserving houses, churches, ships, &c., from lightning, by directing us to fix on the highest parts of these edifices upright rods of iron, made sharp as a needle, and gilt to prevent rusting, and from the foot of these rods a wire down the outside of the building *into the ground*, or down the shrouds of a ship and down her side, till it reaches the water? Would not these pointed rods probably draw the electrical fire silently out of a cloud before it came nigh enough to strike and thereby secure us from that most sudden and terrible mischief.

This suggestion led three years later to the installation in Philadelphia of the first lightning-rod. The proposal simply involved joining the original insulated rod (of Fig. 1 above) to the ground (as in Fig. 2). As stated originally by Franklin, it depended for its success or failure upon the degree to which the upward discharge of electricity between pointed rod and cloud could render harmless the charge on the cloud. The lightning-rod, if it was to work in this manner, could only do so if the point discharge from it did actually neutralize the charge on the cloud to an appreciable extent. In the laboratory experiments which Franklin had made with his electrical machine, earth-connected metal points certainly neutralized electrified bodies placed near to them. But it would seem unlikely that the same thing could happen on the much larger scale of Nature when a puny point, a few tens of feet high, faced a thunder-cloud a mile or more above it.

In actual fact it does not happen. A single point, or for that matter a multitude of points such as the tops of trees in a forest or the poles and chimneys of a town, has little effect upon the charge on the thunderstorm above it. None the less the lightning-rod, as is abundantly proven, has a very real virtue, because it 'attracts' lightning to it (in the manner which will be described in Chapter 5) and can lead a flash to ground without damage to the building to which is it attached.

There has been a good deal of controversy about this question—neutralization versus attraction—of the action of the lightning-conductor. It is interesting to note that Franklin himself was not sure which of these actions was the most significant. He published annually a widely read almanac and calendar of events, into which many of his own proverbs and ideas were put, and in this—*Poor Richard's Almanac* for the year 1753—he wrote:

It has pleased God in His goodness to mankind at length to dis-cover to them the means of securing their habitations and other buildings from mischief by thunder and lightning. The method is this: Provide a small iron rod (it may be of the rod-iron used by the nailers) but of such length that, one end being three or four feet in the moist ground, the other may be six or eight feet above the highest part of the building. To the upper end of the rod fasten about a foot of brass wire the size of a common knitting needle, sharpened to a fine point; the rod may be secured to the house by a few small staples. If the house or barn be long, there may be a rod and point at each end, and a middling wire along the ridge from one to the other. A house thus furnished will not be damaged by lightning, *it being attracted by the points and passing through the metal* without hurting anybody. Vessels, also, having a sharp-pointed rod fixed on the top of their masts, with a wire from the foot of the rod reaching down, round one of the shrouds, to the water, will not be hurt by lightning.

The original of this famous statement is reproduced in Plate II: it will be seen that it was sandwiched between announcements of the dates and places of Quakers' meetings and of the Mayor's courts.

In this statement, as the italicized portion above shows, he definitely plumps for 'attraction'. But in another publication in 1767, fourteen years later, he was not so sure, for he said: 'Thus the pointed rod *either prevents a stroke from the cloud, or if a stroke is made, conducts it to the earth with safety* to the building.'

The argument was not then, nor for 150 years to come, capable of final settlement. But an immediate question of great practical importance had to be decided. If a lightning-rod attracts the lightning-flash, does it attract it to itself or merely to its neighbourhood? For if the latter were even occasionally the case, the installation of a conductor might well be not a protection but a danger. There was doubt at the

time in the minds of many of the best experimenters as to
whether Franklin was not being unduly optimistic in thinking
that he could draw the lightning to the rod itself, and some even
argued with vehemence that points were unwise. Fortunately
he had the courage to make the trial and the energy and ability
to persuade others to do so too.

The First Lightning-conductors

Poor Richard's Almanac had the phenomenal sale, for those
days, of 10,000 copies a year and was widely read. From
1752 onwards many 'Franklin rods' were erected in various
parts of the American colonies. It is fitting that the first successful performance of the rod should have taken place in
Philadelphia, where in 1760 it saved the house of Mr. West,
a merchant, from damage by a direct stroke. The second success was in Charlestown in the same year. By 1764 the rods
were in widespread use on churches and houses in America,
though by some they were thought impious, and a Boston
divine accused them of having been responsible for an earth
tremor which shook Massachusetts in 1755. Franklin's own
house was not struck until 1787, when, in his eighty-first year,
his conductor led Jove's thunderbolt quietly to earth.

The new device was adopted in England in 1760, when the
Eddystone lighthouse, a wooden structure which had previously been set on fire and destroyed as a result of a lightning-
flash, was fitted with a rod. The first English house to be
protected was that of Dr. Watson at Payneshill in 1762. Though
there was much argument amongst experts as to the wisdom
of fitting the conductors with points, successful American
experience with them led to their adoption for the protection
of many public buildings. St. Bride's Church in London having
been severely damaged in 1769, the Dean and Chapter of
St. Paul's addressed a letter to the Royal Society asking their
opinion on the most effective method of fixing electrical conductors to the cathedral. The Society's committee for the purpose included Benjamin Franklin and one Benjamin Wilson,
who was very much opposed to pointed conductors because of

their attractive power. No mention was made of points in the committee's recommendations; they simply advised a complete metallic connexion to join the cross on the lanthorn to the leaden covering of the great dome, the water-pipes then serving as conductors from the roof of the dome to the ground. The rod was installed in 1769, and safely disposed of a lightning-flash three years later.

The disaster to the powder magazine and city of Brescia in 1772 has already been mentioned. This led the British Government to seek advice from the Royal Society on the fitting of conductors to their own large magazines at Purfleet, then totally unprotected. The committee included Franklin, Cavendish, and the same Mr. Benjamin Wilson, who submitted a minority report opposing the use of pointed conductors, which were, however, fitted. A flash of lightning unfortunately hit the magazine soon after the conductors were installed and damaged it slightly.

Although no explosion occurred, the incident added considerably to the heat of the growing controversy about pointed rods, which will be described in the next section. The cause of this particular failure of the protective system is discussed in Chapter 6.

In France the first conductor was erected in 1773 by Professor de Moricau on the building housing the Academy of Sciences at Dijon. The device was not generally adopted for some time owing to the strong opposition of the Abbé Nollet, Professor at the Sorbonne, who held that the attractive action of the rod would do more harm than good.

An interesting figure appears for a moment in the minor history of the subject in France; in 1780 M. Vissery de Bois Vallé put up a conductor on his house at St. Omer, but had to remove it because of the objections of his neighbours. These objections were sustained by the local magistrates, but his advocate took the case to an appeal court, and won it. The successful lawyer was Maximilian de Robespierre, subsequently to become the 'sea-green incorruptible' of Carlyle's *French Revolution*.

The first lightning-conductor to be put up in Germany was installed in 1768 on the house of Dr. Reimarus of Hamburg. Twelve years later 226 buildings of that city and district were protected with rods.

Knobs versus Points

Mr. Strahan:

... You are now my enemy and
                    I am
                        Yours,
                            B. Franklin.
                                (Letter, written but not sent, from Frank-
                                lin to Mr. W. Strahan of London, 1775.)

The opposition of certain European men of science, and in particular that of Benjamin Wilson, Fellow of the Royal Society, to pointed lightning-conductors was very strong. Wilson wrote:

Every point as such, I consider as soliciting the lightning and by that means not only contributing to increase the quantity of every actual discharge, but also frequently occasioning a discharge when it might otherwise not have happened. . . . We may be promoting the very mischief we mean to prevent. Whereas, if instead of pointed, we make use of blunted conductors, these will as effectively answer the purpose of conveying away the lightning safely without that tendency to increase or invite it.

This, says Weld, in his *History of the Royal Society*, was the beginning of the great scientific controversy of knobs versus points. The Declaration of Independence was issued by the American Colonies in 1776 and Franklin was one of the committee who drafted it. We have seen that the powder magazine at Purfleet which had been equipped on Franklin's advice with a conductor fitted with points was none the less struck by lightning and slightly damaged in 1772. The consequent dispute as to the merits and demerits of points became one of politics. George III had the points removed from the Purfleet magazine and from his own palace of St. James, and the East India Company from their powder magazines in Sumatra.

Franklin wrote from Paris, where he represented the American Congress, now at war with Britain:

I have no private interest in the reception of my inventions by the world, having never made, nor proposed to make, the least profit by any of them. The King's changing his pointed conductors for blunt ones is, therefore, a matter of small importance to me. If I had a wish about it, it would be that he had rejected them altogether as ineffectual. For it is only since he thought himself and his family safe from the thunder of Heaven, that he dared to use his own thunder in destroying his innocent subjects.

The advocates of pointed conductors soon became identified with the insurgent American colonists and were considered as rebels. The 'populace and the higher classes of society' took up the scientific quarrel without knowing much about it. George III actually tried to make the Royal Society rescind resolutions they had taken after much acrimonious discussion in favour of pointed conductors in spite of the Purfleet incident. His Majesty, it is declared, had an interview with the President of the Society, Sir John Pringle, who had been a personal friend of Franklin's, during which he 'earnestly entreated' Pringle to use his influence in supporting the 'blunt' Mr. Wilson. To which 'Pringle replied that duty as well as inclination would always induce him to execute His Majesty's wishes to the utmost of his power, but that he could not reverse the laws and operations of Nature'. Shortly after this interview a friend of Franklin's wrote:

> While you, Great George, for knowledge hunt,
> And sharp conductors change for blunt,
>   The nation's out of joint.
> Franklin a wiser course pursues
> And all your thunder useless views
>   By keeping to the point.

Benjamin Wilson was not the only redoubtable opponent of Franklin. The Abbé Nollet went farther than Wilson, and in a memoir read before the Paris Academy of Sciences declared that 'all these iron points . . . are more likely to attract lightning than to save us from it and . . . the idea of dissipating the charge in a thundercloud (by points) is not scientific'.

Many great scientific controversies, as Norman Campbell said of the dispute as to whether light consisted of waves or particles, end in the comforting conclusion that both sides were right, and the lightning-rod controversy is no exception. The Abbé Nollet was right in maintaining that pointed conductors have no appreciable effect on the charge on a cloud, and Wilson was right in saying that blunt conductors are every bit as good as pointed ones. But both were wrong in suggesting that the attractive influence of a lightning-rod is harmful, for experience over two centuries has shown that by this influence the rod gives complete protection to a building within a certain radius. The manner in which it does this will be described in a later chapter, where it will be seen that the last word rested with Franklin when he said:

In every stroke of lightning, I am of opinion that *the stream of the electric fluid* (from the cloud) *will go considerably out of a direct course for the sake of the assistance of good conductors*; and that in this connexion it is actually moving, though silently and imperceptibly, before the explosion, in and among the conductors.

In an attempt to obtain experimental evidence on the value of points, Franklin's rod and kite experiments were extensively repeated. Elaborate kites of various kinds were developed and flown, first with knobs and then with points attached, in an attempt to compare their efficiencies. One kite made by de Romas, a judge of the Court of Nerac in Gascony, was $7\frac{1}{2}$ feet high, and when connected to ground by a copper wire gave sparks 10 feet long 'which made more noise than gunfire'. The results of all this work were, however, inconclusive. It was, moreover, very dangerous, as de Romas himself discovered on one occasion, for the electrical charges and voltages obtained from the clouds are vastly greater than those developed from frictional electrical machines. The electrical fluid, with which Franklin and his friends used to amuse themselves by giving one another shocks, and with which

King Louis XVI had administered 'with prodigious effect' shocks to 200 Carthusian monks holding hands, killed Professor Richmann of St. Petersburg in the course of thunderstorm experiments with an insulated Franklin rod in 1753.

Franklinismus

Notwithstanding the disputations of the learned academies, the new system of lightning-protection was eagerly adopted all over America and Europe. In July 1770 three houses and a merchant-ship were struck in Philadelphia; damage was caused to all except the one house which was equipped with a lightning-rod. In 1777 the recently installed conductor of the much-struck cathedral of Siena took a lightning-flash without any damage to the building. The church of the castle of the Orsinis in the mountains of Carinthia, which had suffered so much from lightning that it was closed during the summer, and had to have its steeple rebuilt twice in eight years, was fitted with a conductor and found to be safe from further damage. The campanile of St. Mark's in Venice, as we have seen, was similarly freed from frequent damage. These and many other successes of the lightning-rod naturally created much excitement.

The introduction of the lightning-rod was a great and historic event, the first practical application of the scientific study of electricity, something of use to mankind after a century and more of rubbing glass and amber rods and 'playing' with electroscopes and Leyden jars. The electric battery, and the electric current as we know it to-day, had not yet appeared, even in scientific laboratories. It was not till 1786 that Galvani in Italy brought it to light by observing the twitching of a frog's legs when the animal was placed on metal plates, and not till 1799 that Volta produced the first electric battery. Franklin's invention, in the greatness of its conception and the considerable economic value of its application, was rightly considered astounding. He had snatched the sceptre not merely from George III but from Jove himself.

The further history of the lightning-rod contains many

curious chapters, for its development was pursued with a good deal of misapplied zeal.

The chief German exponent of 'Franklinismus', Dr. Reimarus of Hamburg, argued with great weight that a deep earth connexion for a lightning-conductor was not only unnecessary but quite wrong. Since it was commonly observed, said he, that the passage of lightning through a tree caused steam to be suddenly produced and hence an explosion which could split the trunk, a similar explosive generation of steam was to be feared if the lower end of a lightning-rod was placed deep into wet soil. He therefore advised that the earth connexion should be made to the drier top-soil by shallow wiring. This advice was widely accepted in Germany, and it has been stated that it led to thousands of faulty and dangerous installations, many of which persisted until the late nineteenth century.

Benjamin Wilson himself was so suspicious of the attractive power of the rod that he went so far as to advise in 1764 that the rod should not extend above the building at all but should end in a blunt point or knob below the roof. He was, however, outdone by others, who considered that the attractive action of the rod could be reversed, and the lightning-stroke repelled, by fitting the tip of the conductor with insulating glass balls. Such balls were fitted to the vane-rod on the steeple of Christ Church, Doncaster. The result was hardly satisfactory, for the steeple was demolished by a lightning-flash not long after.

'Experts' on points of various kinds had an excellent opportunity in the design and sale of elaborate types of conductor, including crowns and diadems and spears of special, and according to their arguments essential, shapes. One such specialist is recorded as supplying reversed or downwardly directed points at the base of the rod, to discharge the electrical current more efficiently into the ground.

A very elaborate arrangement of points to enable the conductor to discharge the clouds most effectively was advocated in England by Lord Mahon, and became known as the Stanhope system. Similar structures—immense Franklin rods with many points and known as Electrical Niagaras—were erected in many parts of France in the belief that they would divert thunderstorms from growing crops and would prevent the falling, or even the formation, of hail. In spite of much public support the idea was not taken up by the French Government.

A Moravian priest, Procope Divisch, who put up an elaborately branched rod on the top of his house at Prinditz in 1754, and for whom it has been claimed that he anticipated Franklin's invention, was not so fortunate in his public. The peasants of the village tore it to pieces on the grounds that it was responsible for the prevailing drought.

In 1830 a Mr. J. Murray propounded an ingenious tubular conductor which was to be fitted with a hole near its tip to allow the lightning to run down inside the tube and pass into a water-filled stone trough below. Such an earth-connexion— to the inside of a cemented water-cistern, with no proper communication to the ground—was responsible for considerable damage to the lighthouse at Fécamp in France when it was struck by lightning in the year 1867.

Two valuable developments emerged from this welter of ideas. The first was the system of earthing the conductor by burying a copper or zinc plate in a pit filled with charcoal, thereby enabling the discharge to spread rapidly and easily through the earth. This system, which is widely used to-day, was first proposed by a fellow citizen of Franklin, Professor Patterson, whose other suggestion, the use of indestructible graphite instead of metal for points, has, however, gone into limbo. The second useful development was the introduction of copper for the conductors. This was the contribution of English investigators, though the Continent long continued to use iron.

The use of copper caused a controversy as to the relative merits of tubes and strips, in the course of which the chief English expert, Sir William Snow Harris, came into angry conflict with Michael Faraday. Harris designed the lightning-protection system for the new Houses of Parliament at Westminster in 1855 and fitted copper conductors, 2 inches in diameter and $\frac{1}{8}$-inch thick at a cost of £2,000. The tubes proved difficult to erect and were very easily damaged when once they were up. Faraday pointed out that no very clear reasons had been given why solid-strip conductors should be inferior to tubes, and advised against tubes in future on the grounds of cost and liability to damage.

The Radius of Protection of the Rod

As the Franklin system spread, it became obvious from experience that a good lightning-conductor meant protection for a building, but it was not clear over what distance this protection extended. Franklin himself was properly reticent on this point; only experience could decide. The first official statement on the subject came in 1833 from the Academy of Sciences in Paris, which, after considering the experience of sixty years, proposed the adoption of a horizontal distance equal to twice the height of the rod above the ground (Charles's rule). In the case of a church steeple, however, the height was to be taken as the height above the main roof, not above the ground, and the radius of protection as this height alone. In 1854 this rule was revised by the Academy, and the protective radius considered greater if the roof of the church or building had some metal on it. In 1867 the Academy pronounced against pointed conductors, and stated that in its opinion points were of no value.

Much discussion has taken place on this important question of the radius of protection. Perhaps the most direct evidence has been provided by an analysis, published by Walter, of the protective influence of church steeples and other high buildings in the old city of Hamburg upon lower houses in their neighbourhood. This information was obtained from the books of insurance companies who had paid out claims for lightning damage to houses in the city. Between 1912 and 1932 there were twenty-five such claims. In only four of these cases were the houses concerned closer to nearby church steeples than twice the height of the steeple above their roofs, and there was no case where a house was hit if it was nearer to a steeple than the difference in height itself.

The most recent view on the radius of protection of the rod is discussed in Chapter 6.

The Application of Lightning-conductors to Wooden Ships

Mention has been made of Sir William Snow Harris's proposals to reduce the serious damage caused by lightning to ships by fitting them with conductors. Harris was a Plymouth doctor who, at the age of 38, gave up medicine for electrical studies, to which he made important contributions. Although a Royal Commission had recommended general adoption of his conductors by the Navy, the Admiralty continued to offer various objections to his system. Captains of ships had already had many years of experience of an unsatisfactory form of lightning-conductor due to Dr. Watson of Payneshill, and had abandoned it on the grounds that the cure was worse than the disease. Watson's conductor, first suggested in 1762, consisted of 'links of quarter-inch copper rod united by small eyes at each end and the whole attached to a hempen line and hung from the masthead, the lower end dipping into the sea'. This arrangement, though reasonable enough in theory, proved extremely troublesome in practice, damaging top-masts and rigging in heavy gales. The seamen who had to fit up the linked conductor when a storm threatened were in danger of being struck before it was finally fixed, and in many instances the conductor caused damage or loss of life because it was broken or because the end was not in the sea when the ship was struck. Three men were struck dead while fitting these linked conductors on board an American ship-of-war on the Mississippi, and many casualties occurred from the same cause on French and British ships. The links often proved too thin to carry the current of the discharge, and the poor contact afforded by the 'eyes' caused side-flashes from the conductor to the ship. Captain Childs, who commanded H.M.S. *Andromache* for four years, stated that during that time 'scarcely a day passed without the conductors requiring repair'. Wire cordage was introduced on French ships for the same purpose but suffered from similar defects in use.

To avoid these troubles Harris proposed to turn the masts themselves into conductors by nailing overlapping copper strips all the way down each mast, the plates to be joined to bands of copper connected to the keels and keelson and to the metal parts of the hull. The system was actually adopted by the Russian Navy before Harris had succeeded in overcoming opposition against it in England. The Admiralty eventually gave in, but between 1829 and 1843 no less than forty-seven naval vessels not so fitted were damaged more or less severely.

The need for special lightning-protection for wooden ships declined during the nineteenth century with the rapid development of the iron ship from 1860 onwards and of the steel mast and hull between 1880 and 1890. By 1870 the tonnage of iron shipping built in the United Kingdom was more than five times that of wooden ones, and from that date onwards the protection of wooden ships against lightning ceased to be of major importance. The Harris system is still to be seen on some wooden-masted ships, and is insisted upon by insurance companies if such ships do not carry a radio aerial which can be earthed by connecting it to a metal plate below the water-line or to the metal hull during thunderstorms.

The 'Return Shock' and the Galvanic Battery

If the reader will return for a moment to Fig. 2 on p. 19, he will see that the charged cloud shown there has produced an 'induced' positive charge at the top of the earthed Franklin rod. When a lightning-flash discharges the cloud to earth at any point, near or far, this induced charge must disappear by flowing down the rod to earth. A person standing in the open and very close to the point struck by a lightning-flash will perforce be himself a Franklin rod, and the induced charge on his hat or head will similarly flow rapidly to earth through his body when the flash is over. This effect, which is known as the 'return shock', may cause death from lightning without the person concerned being directly struck.

About the year 1786, Galvani, a physician of Bologna, was studying the convulsive motions produced by the 'return shock' upon a frog's leg which, when dissected so as to connect the crural nerves to the Franklin rod, he found to form a very sensitive indicator of lightning-flashes. While experimenting with a 'rod' in the form of an iron wire, similar to a modern wireless aerial, he observed convulsive kicks from his detector on a day when there were no thunderstorms about at all. He traced the effect to his having attached a brass hook to the iron wire. The dissimilar metals, whenever he earthed the rod, created what we to-day call a galvanic battery. The discovery was correctly explained by Volta, Professor in the University of Pavia, whose voltaic cell, produced in 1799, gave the world its first source of electric current at low voltage, relegated the rubbed glass cylinders of Franklin's epoch to the museum of curiosities, and ushered in the great developments of electrical knowledge of the nineteenth century.

3

THE FORMS TAKEN BY LIGHTNING AND SOME OF ITS EFFECTS

'. . . as it nearer comes,
And rolls its awful burden on the wind,
The lightnings flash a larger curve, and more
The noise astounds; till overhead a sheet
Of livid flame discloses wide; then shuts
And opens wider.'

JAMES THOMSON, *The Seasons.*

Cloud-flashes

IN the diagrams of charged thunder-clouds on pp. 18 and 19 they were shown as carrying positive charges on their tops and negative charges on their bases. This distribution of electric charges of opposite sign, one above the other, is characteristic of charged clouds, and often produces lightning-flashes within the cloud itself. These cloud-flashes neutralize the two charged regions by bringing the positive and negative charges together. They are often, but wrongly, called 'cloud-to-cloud' discharges. The bright channels of cloud-flashes are as a rule hidden from the eye by the great mass of water-drops and snow and ice particles in the cloud. Except for odd bits near the edge all that can usually be seen of them is a diffuse general illumination, a sheet of brightly lit-up cloud, and so this type of flash is often called sheet-lightning.

Cloud-flashes are most common in thunderstorms whose bases are so high above the ground that it would seem to be easier for a discharge to pass from the lower to the upper charged part of the cloud, or vice versa, than to take the longer route from the base of the cloud to the ground. They are very much more frequent in the drier parts of southern Africa than elsewhere, for in such semi-arid regions the cloud-base forms higher above the ground than in countries where the air is not so dry. In Great Britain, where thunder-cloud bases are about 1,000 yards above the ground, flashes within the cloud are about equal in number to flashes from the cloud to the ground. In parts of South Africa cloud-flashes outnumber ground-flashes by ten to one. Were it not for this the large number of thunderstorms in such areas would be a serious cause of death and fire.

Air Discharges and Bolts from the Blue

A type of lightning-flash frequently seen in dry countries comes out from the bottom of the cloud and branches profusely

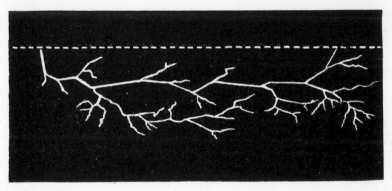

FIG. 4

into the air below it without reaching the ground. It is not always directed vertically downwards; sometimes it may take a very long, almost horizontal, journey in the air below the cloud and end either in the air or in another part of the cloud-base five or ten miles from its starting-point. In the latter case the flash which started from a concentration of negative charge ends in a patch of positive charge brought down from the top of the cloud by falling rain or produced by a mechanism described later in Chapter 7, p. 126. One such meandering flash thirty miles long has been reported.

Very occasionally these wandering air discharges turn earthwards at their ends and hit the ground far away from their starting-point. Flashes of this kind must be responsible for the ancient belief that lightning sometimes appears out of a clear sky as a 'bolt from the blue'. I investigated one such case in which the people who observed it were educated farmers and prepared to swear affidavits that no storm was anywhere near them when the bolt fell. They were working in a deep valley, from which they could not see the distant cloud from which the flash originated.

A type of air discharge which is rarely reported, but which probably often occurs, has the appearance of a glow from the top of a thunder-cloud to the upper air.

Forked Lightning

The best-known form of the lightning-flash is the discharge to ground, commonly called forked or streak lightning, which appears to pass nearly vertically downwards along a zigzag path, with forks or branches which are almost always directed downwards. A good photograph of forked lightning shows, as indicated in Fig. 5, that it is much more branched than is usually judged by the eye, for the observer is dazzled by the brilliance of the main channel of the discharge.

In Europe and North America the length of the flash which can be seen below the cloud is usually from a half to three-quarters of a mile. In South Africa the visible vertical length is often twice or three times as great. The actual length of the channel is greater still, for the flash not only moves along a zigzag path below the cloud, often inclined to the vertical, but also starts from a charged region some distance within the cloud itself.

Although a flash to ground usually strikes the ground at one place only, it is sometimes found that two or more forks occur at the bottom of the channel, both of which hit objects such as houses or trees. This effect is due in most cases to an alteration in the lower portion of the channel in different strokes of the series which makes up the flash. McEachron has described a case in which the first stroke of the flash struck a building 360 ft. high and 1,200 ft. away from the Empire State Building, which was the target for the next three strokes, the change in

Fig. 5

path occurring 655 ft. above it. The reason for this is discussed on p. 76.

Recurrent and Triggered Flashes

When the shape of the channel and the branches of each of a series of flashes to ground are carefully watched, one sometimes observes a very marked similarity in the form of successive flashes. On a number of occasions I have seen such a series from one particular part of a cloud and noted that their general form, including sharp bends and branches, was repeated at intervals of about half a minute about six times over. Since there is no possibility of the original channel remaining 'alive' for so long, the conclusion to be drawn from such recurrent forms is that the cloud was charging up very regularly after each flash so that the electrical conditions inside it and in the air below it were very much the same for each successive flash.

Another occasional regularity, which is to be explained in the same way, is sometimes seen in the case of the 'triggered' or 'sympathetic' discharge which occurs when a flash from one point in the cloud is followed nearly simultaneously by one from another point or even from a nearby cloud. A good case has been described by Champion in which three flashes to ground appeared from one part of a cloud practically simultaneously and were followed about fifteen seconds later by a fourth some distance away, the whole process repeating itself regularly many times. The discharge of one portion of a cloud can reasonably be expected to make it easier for another portion to reach the electric tension needed for it also to discharge, and if the cloud is charging up very regularly the process could be repeated over and over again.

Separate Strokes

A conspicuous feature of the flash to ground is the flicker in the light it gives out. The whole flash lasts for about a second, but it is not discharging at the same rate for a full second. The flash consists of a number of separate partial discharges or strokes, each lasting a very short time, which follow one another intermittently at intervals of about a thirtieth part of a second. It is this intermittent illumination of the channel which causes the flicker. The most frequent number of separate strokes in a discharge is three, but as many as forty-seven have been recorded. Separate strokes usually follow the same channel, since the heated air produced by the first stroke provides a convenient path for subsequent ones to follow, though at the bottom end of its channel a discharge not infrequently takes an alternative route if the interval of time between successive strokes is abnormally long.

Ribbon Lightning

On rare occasions, if a strong wind is blowing, the separate strokes of a near flash can be seen by the unaided eye or recorded on a fixed camera. The channel which they follow and

FIG. 6

which remains as a zigzag 'rope' of very hot air in the intervals between strokes, perhaps carrying a weaker but continuous discharge of electricity between cloud and ground, can be shifted by the wind sufficiently for the successive strokes to be separated in space from one another. The appearance of the flash so produced gives it the name of ribbon lightning (fig. 6).

Since a wind blowing at 18 miles an hour at right angles to the channel would shift it by 26 feet in one second and so provide space for a ribbon of many strokes, it is perhaps surprising that ribbon lightning is not seen and photographed more often.

The answer appears to be that the eye, and the camera lens, too, cannot perceive the detail of (or in technical language, resolve) such a ribbon-flash unless it is within a few miles of the observer, and that when it is so near the brilliance of the flash itself is apt to make observation of detail very difficult.

How Wide is the Channel ?

When a good photograph of a ribbon lightning-flash is available and it is certain from the clearness of objects in the foreground that the camera which took it was perfectly steady, it can be used to find the widths of the channels of the separate discharges. This cannot be done unless the channels of separate strokes are clearly separated because in the usual case the wind, which is always blowing, produces an unresolved 'ribbon' effect which is responsible for an apparent widening of the channel. In one study of a ribbon-flash the author found the average diameter of eleven separate strokes in a ribbon to be six inches. This is the only direct evidence we have for the diameter of the lightning-channel in the air; that it is likely to be about this figure has been estimated from the diameter of holes found in objects struck by lightning and from the sand fulgurites described on p. 57, which are a few inches wide.

Some Inadmissible Forms of Lightning

Photographs are occasionally taken, and often published in the press, which show lightning-forms of a very peculiar kind which are not known as ever having been seen by the naked eye. Amongst these are pictures of snake-like discharges of large diameter, often contorted in coils and otherwise winding about in a manner which seems hardly natural. These discharges are usually so disposed with reference to the objects in the foreground of the picture that it is clear they would have proved at the least very uncomfortable to the photographer if they had really existed. Though the taker of the picture is naturally reluctant to accept an explanation based upon an error on his part, it can generally be proved that these terrible-looking discharges are false images caused by stray lights, torches, or motor-car headlights. Their coils arise from casual movement either of the lights or of the camera, all unobserved in the excitement of taking the pictures of real lightning. Publication of such abnormal pictures in the press is, of course, not a guarantee of their genuineness.

Saint Elmo's Fire

I boarded the King's ship; now in the beak,
Now in the waist, the deck, in every cabin,
I flamed amazement; sometime I'd divide
And burn in many places; on the topmast
The yards and bowsprit, would I flame distinctly
Then meet and join.

The Tempest, Act I, Scene II.

A faint luminous glow is often seen at night at the tops of the masts of ships when a charged cloud is overhead. It goes by the name of St. Elmo's Fire, for St. Elmo (Erasmus) was the patron saint of Mediterranean sailors, and his fort and point to this day guard the Grand Harbour of Malta. English sailors called the glows a 'corposant', from *corpo santo* (the body of the saint).

That the passage from Shakespeare quoted at the head of this section is not mere poetic imagining can be seen from the experience of Captain A. Simpson, of the steamer *Moravian*, whose log for 30 December 1902, off Cape Verde, states: 'For fully an hour the sky was one blaze of lightning, and wire ropes, mastheads, yardarms, derrick-ends, &c. were lighted up. All the stays seemed to have glow-lamps three to four feet apart and the mastheads and yardarms a bright light at their extremities.' An extraordinary sound was heard all the time 'as if several thousands of cicadas had taken up their quarters in the rigging, or like the crackling of burning grass or twigs'.

The appearance of St. Elmo's Fire has always been regarded by sailors as a good omen, indicating the end of a storm. It is related that Christopher Columbus raised the spirits of his men during a tempest on his voyage to America by pointing to the 'holy fire' at the masthead, which foretold the end of their troubles. This belief goes back to the time of the Greeks, when

Castor and Pollux were the patron gods of sailors, and the fire was called after their sister, Helen of Troy. It is a fact that the strongest winds and highest seas come before the thunderstorm itself, and when the storm is well overhead and its electrification is capable of producing St. Elmo's Fire, the worst is over.

FIG. 7

The luminous glow arises from the electrical discharge from points, described on p. 17, and is of the same nature as the light from a 'neon' street sign.

Very strong glows of this kind are to be seen when thunderstorms pass over high mountain peaks. The bottom of the cloud is then close to the ground and can at times even be in the valley below the peak itself, so that the electric fields producing point-discharge are exceptionally intense. At such times, observers in the Alps have reported most impressive crackling, luminous flames, several inches long, passing upwards from their heads and fingers. The glow from the head takes the form of a halo, and pointed objects such as ice-axes are tipped with flame. It is possible that the burning yet unconsumed bush encountered by Moses on Mount Sinai was due to a glow of this kind, which, as described by Humphreys, can produce a weird effect on a lonely cattle ranch 'by turning every steer into a devil with flaming horns'. The glow is said to be more extensive when the overhead cloud is negatively charged below than when it is positive; its colour is described as reddish in the former case and bluish in the latter—which is, however, probably not very frequent.

Very powerful glows of the same kind can also occur during severe duststorms, when the air and the dust in it are strongly electrified by the frictional rubbing together of the dust particles by the wind. During the eruption of Mont Pelée, in Martinique, volcanic dust shot upwards in large quantities and caused lightning to play about the summit of the mountain.

It is related in a scientific paper written in 1764 by Giovanni Bianchini that the occurrence of point discharge was used 'from time immemorial' to give warning of approaching storms at the Castle of Duino in the Julian Alps. A lance with a wooden shaft was erected on the battlements and the soldier of the watch had orders to touch the point of it to his halberd from time to time. If sparks occurred, he would ring a bell to warn the workers in the field that a storm was imminent. The lance, being insulated by its wooden shaft, would acquire its charge in the same way as the insulated Franklin rod of Fig. 1 on p. 18.

St. Elmo's Fire often shows itself very prominently when an aircraft is flying through charged clouds, the propellers and edges of the machine becoming the source of glows of great size and intensity. Such point-discharge of electricity from an aircraft can cause serious interference with the radio-receiving and direction-finding equipment on the aircraft, and thus be a danger to navigation. The 'fire' discharges intermittently and gives rise to intense crackling 'static' noise in the radio-receivers, generally called 'precipitation static'. The best remedy for it appears to be to provide the machine with a sufficient number of suitably placed point dischargers so that the electricity collected by the aircraft can be got rid of quickly and easily to the surrounding air in the form of quiet and continuous glow-discharge.

Glows from the Tops of Thunder-clouds

It is doubtful whether actual lightning-flashes ever pass from the top of a thunder-cloud upwards to the upper air. Some reported cases of flashes like this were probably horizontal or even downward air-discharges from the cloud-tops, for it is very difficult to be sure that the discharge is upward unless one is a long way off from it. But there are well-established observations of glows like St. Elmo's Fire having been seen at the tops of clouds. One remarkable case, reported by M. D. Laurenson from New Zealand in 1936, took the form of a brilliant ball of light at the top of a bank of cloud. This pulsated in size and intensity for over fifteen minutes, in the course of which time it gave out a very bright greenish-white radiance which lit up the whole of the upper surface of the cloud-bank and illuminated the country-side around as if thousands of searchlights were in action. Another form of glow-discharge passing from the top of the cloud to the upper air has been seen to occur regularly at the same time as a flash to ground. Further observations of phenomena of this nature would be valuable in connexion with the study of the mechanism of thunder-cloud electrification.

Lightning-flashes to Aircraft

Lightning-flashes to aircraft flying through or under clouds are by no means uncommon. A sub-committee of the United States National Advisory Committee for Aeronautics has collected information on 169 cases of such discharges over the period from March 1935 to December 1944, less than nine years. The majority of these discharges took place while the aircraft were flying in cloud, though only about half the clouds were noticed to be giving rise to lightning before the aircraft were struck, which indicates that an aircraft can sometimes trigger off a flash which would not have occurred had the air-craft not been there. The principal types of cloud from which or inside which the aircraft were struck were cumulo-nimbus, cumulus, and strato-cumulus, terms which, as shown in Chapter 7, reflect the different stages in the development of the thunder-cloud. The fully developed cumulo-nimbus cloud was much more likely to give trouble than the other two. Instances of discharges hitting an aircraft flying outside or below the cloud itself were almost all associated with active thunderstorms of cumulo-nimbus type. The altitude range in which lightning most frequently struck these aircraft was from 4,000 to 9,000 feet above ground. In more than half the reported cases they were flying through rain mixed with some form of frozen water (snow, hail, or sleet) at temperatures near or below the freezing-point. From other evidence this is the region of a cloud where the greatest electrical tension would be expected.

In most cases a very pronounced display of St. Elmo's Fire takes place before the aircraft is struck. The glow appears most frequently for a minute before the flash, though on a few occasions there was only a fraction of a second between the two, and in one remarkable case the aircraft travelled for $4\frac{1}{2}$ hours with a glowing halo round it before it was struck.

Some of the reports of St. Elmo's Fire on aircraft describe very impressive displays, involving luminous streamers ten to fifteen feet long and six inches wide, projecting forward from the propellers and the wing-tips like forked fingers. At times the engines have been enveloped in glowing halos, and at others the wind-shields have been sufficiently electrified by contact with ice and sleet to glow all over.

The path taken by a lightning-flash in passing through an aeroplane is most usually the longest one possible. In the great majority of cases the flash has passed from wing-tip to wing-tip, or from nose to tail, or from nose or tail to wing-tip. If the aircraft has a trailing wire radio aerial below it this is usually involved, with resulting damage to the wire and to the radio installation if this has not been 'earthed' to the main frame of the plane. All this information shows, as would be expected, that the flash uses the aircraft to by-pass or short-circuit as much of the more resistant air as it can. A survey of the damage caused by such strokes shows it to be most frequently at the extremities of the aircraft—the wings and ailerons, the tail, trailing aerial, and propellers.

All the evidence goes to show that the extent of the material damage to aircraft made entirely of metal is not usually serious. On the other hand, aircraft which employ fabric or wood in their construction, or all-metal aircraft in which the metallic parts are not properly connected (bonded) together, are often subject to considerable damage, and for them a lightning-stroke constitutes a definite hazard.

Apart, however, from minor damage to its extremities an all-metal aircraft struck by lightning may be placed in difficulties by the effect of the flash on its navigating instruments. As mentioned above, the radio communication and direction-finding equipment is readily put out of action by the discharge unless it has been protected. It is also not unusual for the magnetic compass to become unreliable either through the direct action of the discharge on its magnets or through magnetization produced by the heavy current passing through or near steel in the aircraft.

When an aircraft is struck at night the brilliance of the flash may temporarily blind the pilot, generally only for a few seconds but sometimes for several minutes. Since the machine is usually flying in very turbulent air there is a risk that it may be in danger during the time that the pilot is momentarily handicapped by the effect of the flash on his eyes and on his general reactions. Some authorities recommend, therefore, that in flying through or near thunder-clouds the instrument panel lights in the cockpit should be brightened and the automatic pilot, if not already engaged, be put ready to take over control. Both upward and downward winds reach very high values in certain parts of thunder-clouds, and unless the aircraft is under control it can meet with a dangerous situation. Tests carried out in Florida in 1946 and 1947 by agencies of the United States Government (The Thunderstorm Project) showed that on occasion an aircraft flying at 150 miles an hour could be displaced upwards by as much as 6,000 feet in flying through one cloud or could be pushed down by 2,300 feet. These values are exceptional, for the average figures are about half those quoted, and for faster machines they are still less, but they show the degree of turbulence which is likely to be prevalent at the moment the aircraft is struck. Incidentally, the machines were hit twenty-one times by lightning during the two summer seasons of flying and suffered no serious damage at all.

The general instructions issued to pilots who may encounter thunderstorms are too detailed to quote here, but amount to saying that they are very definitely things to avoid. If they cannot be flown over or flown round, it is recommended that flight below them should be made with an adequate clearance of at least 2,000 feet between the cloud-base and the aircraft and of 4,000 feet between the aircraft and the ground. The heavy rain-curtain, the roll clouds near the cloud-base, and the region of strong updraughts and downdraughts are, according to the committee mentioned at the start of this section, all to be specially avoided.

Much activity is at present being shown in the development of special radar equipment to warn aircraft, particularly those travelling at night, of clouds ahead which are in a condition to give rise to lightning-discharges or may be very turbulent.

Ball Lightning

There are many circumstantial accounts of the appearance of a moving fire-ball during a thunderstorm. The diameter of the ball varies in these accounts from $\frac{1}{2}$ inch to 6 feet and its shape, though usually spherical, is occasionally described as oval. Its colour is variously given as white, red, yellow, and blue. Its life is usually only a few seconds, though sometimes it is said to last for several minutes. On reaching the ground or moving over it fire-balls are generally said to bounce a great deal and often to burst with a loud report, leaving holes at their final resting-place. They are usually described as travelling downwards, but some few have been recorded as shooting upwards like rockets, which, of course, they may actually have been if a practical joker had known that someone was looking out for them. The speed of movement of a fire-ball varies in different accounts from a walk to a run.

In practically all these accounts the ball is seen either at the moment when a very near lightning-flash takes place or just after one. Most of the reported cases are extremely likely to have been caused by optical illusion, since the retina of the eye, when dazzled by a nearby flash seen out of the corner of the eye, retains a residual image of the nature of a luminous ball of light. Moreover, anyone who is close to a flash of light ning is hardly in a position to give a reliable account of what happened, and stories of fire-balls passing down chimneys and bouncing round the house with a sulphurous smell must be treated with considerable reserve.

It appears that no professional observers of the weather, such as meteorologists, have ever seen a fire-ball, though they must have watched, in all, many tens of thousands of lightning flashes. When the many other cases of reported fire-balls are examined, it is found that the few convincing accounts have practically all been given by observers who were involved in thunderstorms on high mountains like the Alps. In such circumstances it is more than possible that what was seen was St. Elmo's Fire, either in a very developed form or in a form not previously known. St. Elmo's Fire *inside* a dry wooden hut on a mountain top is not at all unlikely and has, indeed, been reported. Moreover, in the intense and rapidly changing electric fields sometimes encountered on Alpine peaks the bright glows of St. Elmo's Fire could easily appear to jump from point to point and give the illusion of a moving fireball. There are no reliable reports of ball lightning in South Africa, in spite of the high frequency of other forms of lightning there.

Various theories have been put forward to explain the phenomenon, but in the absence of really reliable observations of a fire-ball or of laboratory experiments which can produce it artificially, they are not at present of much interest. The

American meteorologist, W. J. Humphreys, has examined 280 specially collected personal accounts of ball lightning and has found that all except two or three are explicable as the effects of near flashes or of St. Elmo's Fire. He considers that these accounts did not contain a single certain case of an authentic fire-ball. If it exists at all, it is an extremely uncommon type of electric discharge like 'rocket' and 'beaded' lightning—equally rare forms, whose names adequately describe them.

Some Mistaken Beliefs

There are a number of prevalent but erroneous beliefs about the places where lightning strikes. One is that lightning never strikes twice in the same place. Elevated objects, however, like the campanile of St. Mark in Venice or the Washington Monument in the capital of the United States are struck time and again. The Empire State Building, which towers 1,250 feet into the air in New York, is known to have been hit by lightning sixty-eight times in three years. For reasons which we shall discuss later in this book lightning does not always strike the highest point in a large area, but it strikes it more often than at any other point.

It is generally believed that lightning frequently strikes on South African kopjes (isolated little hills) because it is 'attracted' by the magnetic ironstone of which their tops are formed. There is no scientific basis for this belief; although ironstone is a better conductor than ordinary sedimentary rocks, lightning strikes the hills because they are the highest points in the neighbourhood and for the same reason that it strikes chimneys and trees.

Another prevalent, and, I believe, erroneous belief is that chimneys with fires burning beneath them are exceptionally likely to be struck, since the hot air has some measure of electrical conductivity and effectively extends the chimney farther into the air. The small conductivity of the hot gases from a chimney is, however, most unlikely to exercise much effect upon the path of the flash. A report on lightning damage made by the Department of Lands in Schleswig-Holstein in 1884 stated that chimneys were frequently struck but that, in contradiction to widespread belief, it made no difference whether they were smoking or not.

More recent evidence on this question comes from the investigations on the damage to 169 aircraft which have been mentioned on p. 47. If hot gases played any important part in determining the path followed by a flash, one would expect that the hot engine exhaust-gases would lead flashes to the engine exhausts and cowling. But, actually, out of 370 separate parts which were found to have been damaged on these aircraft, the exhausts are not mentioned at all and the engines only once, when they 'cut out occasionally for a few minutes' after the flash had caused considerable damage to the electrical system of the aircraft by entering through a trailing wire aerial 200 feet long.

It is often maintained that a closed bell-tent is attractive to lightning because of the hot air rising from it. Dr. H. A. Spencer, in his book, *Lightning, Lightning Stroke and its Treatment* (Ballière, Tyndall & Cox, 1932), devotes an interesting chapter to a surprisingly large number of cases observed by him during the Boer War, in which troops and others living in bell-tents were electrocuted during thunderstorms. In all these cases the danger apparently arose from the wooden tent-pole, and the deaths resulted from electricity passing from the pole to persons touching it or very near to it. No tent was ever set on fire, though a ragged hole in the canvas, about six inches in diameter, was generally found round the spot where the top of the pole passed through the tent. It is difficult to accept the view that these deaths were caused by direct lightning-strokes to the tent-poles, for if this were the case the poles would have been shattered and the tents often set on fire; neither event is reported by Dr. Spencer. Their absence strongly suggests that the electric discharges which caused the deaths of so many persons near tent-poles were due to an accumulation of electric charge on the metal cap of the pole and perhaps also on the damp tent, in exactly the same manner as electric charge accumulated on the insulated iron rod in Franklin's experiment described on p. 17 and illustrated in Fig. 1. The wooden part of the pole below would act as an insulator like the glass used in the experiment of 1752, and a very dangerous spark could be drawn from the pole. I have obtained a disconcertingly powerful shock when a storm was overhead by touching my fingers to a small tree which had been mounted on insulators, as described in Chapter 8.

The jagged hole at the top of the tent is also more indicative of relatively mild sparks, burning away the canvas to get to the ground, than of a direct lightning-flash. The other persons in the tents, who were not near the pole and were not seriously injured, quite naturally described the sparks as lightning-discharges, but it is not likely that any of them would have survived if this had really been the case.

Buildings and Trees

Some interesting information about the frequency with which various types of buildings are struck is to be found in an analysis of the statistics of lightning damage caused by 405 flashes to buildings of various kinds in Schleswig-Holstein during the ten years from 1874 to 1884. These are summarized in the table below:

Type of building struck	Percentage of total strikes
Houses with solid roofs	1·0
Houses with thatched roofs	2·5
Churches	40·0
Windmills	54·5
Factory buildings and chimneys	2·0

From these figures it is clear that churches and windmills were about thirty times more attractive to lightning than houses. There is an obvious explanation for this in their much greater height above ground and, in the case of windmills in particular, in their isolated position in flat country.

The figures indicate that houses with thatched roofs were twice as vulnerable as houses with solid roofs. This has probably nothing to do with the thatch itself, but again such houses would be mainly country homes and farm barns which are isolated in the open.

Trees which are struck and damaged by lightning are commonly injured by the scored path the discharge makes in the outside bark. This is often a spiral groove, but sometimes the whole of the bark on one side is blown off. Some writers have attributed the scoring effect to a stream of water running down one side of the trunk and wetting the bark. When converted into steam by the heat of the discharge this water could blow away the bark along its line of flow. If such a stream of water is not present or is not easily available to carry the discharge, the electric current may pass through the sap of the tree and the resulting steam may shatter the whole trunk explosively. In support of these ideas a Captain McLean showed, in a report published in 1890, that of many trees examined by him the only ones to be completely shattered by lightning were struck before rain fell; those struck after rain were not shattered but scored outside, with some of the bark blown off.

This may be the explanation of the susceptibility of the oak to damage by lightning and the frequent occurrence of the 'blasted' oak. An investigation carried out in Germany in 1899 over fifty thousand acres of forest-land showed that though oaks comprised 11 per cent. of the trees they were damaged by lightning so much more frequently than any other kind that they constituted 58 per cent. of all the lightning casualties. The rough bark of the oak would make a continuous stream of water down the trunk during rain less likely than would the smooth bark of trees like the beech. In consequence, a lightning-discharge would blow up an oak explosively but only score the bark of a beech. Actually, beeches made up 70 per cent. of the forests but only about 6 per cent. of the total casualties from lightning, so that an oak was sixty-two times as likely to be damaged as a beech.

Lightning is a serious cause of forest fires. In Oregon and Washington in the North-west United States, 5,500 forest fires were reported to have been caused by flashes over the six years from 1925 to 1931, and as many as 250 'lightning' fires have developed on one day.

The Spread of the Lightning-discharge through the Ground

When lightning strikes dry ground, through which it is not easily conducted away, the discharge current does not spread evenly through the earth but is concentrated in those layers which conduct electricity better than others. If there is a buried water-pipe or underground cable in the neighbourhood of the point struck, the current will tend to flow along such a good conductor. This preference for good conductors is, of course, not always welcomed. Many underground telephone cables have been damaged by it, and the Municipality of Pretoria recently encountered considerable trouble from it when lightning-currents in a poorly conducting (dolomitic) area frequently chose to flow down one of their main water pipe-lines. This pipe-line is of reinforced concrete with iron wire reinforcement, and therefore well able to carry lightning-currents until these reach the joints between sections, which have no metallic connexions across them. At such joints the pipe was sometimes severely damaged by the huge spark which took place. The trouble has been cured, to date at any rate, by providing an alternative path for the current in the form of a copper wire attached to the outside of the pipe.

The same tendency for the lightning-current to flow along good conductors in the ground accounts for the following story told by Dr. Spencer in the book already mentioned.

An elderly gentleman and his son were walking arm-in-arm one night, outside their hotel, on the outskirts of a village in the Transvaal, when a flash of lightning struck the ground about two hundred yards away from them, just as they were walking over an outcrop of ironstone. They received a shock which threw them to the ground locked in each other's embrace, and rolled about upon the ground for some minutes, unable to disentangle themselves or to call out. Finally, some people outside the hotel, thinking they were fighting, separated them and assisted them to their feet, still unable to explain what had occurred. Arriving on the scene soon afterwards,

I found that they had regained their power of speech and were able to discuss the occurrence. They explained that their legs had suddenly ceased to support them and they found themselves rolling upon the ground with flexed limbs. . . . Neither of them showed any burns or other evidences of having been struck by lightning, but their muscles were cramped and sore. . . . Next morning, on visiting the spot where the lightning had struck the ground, I found an outcrop of ironstone similar to that outside the hotel; as I was able to trace it across the intervening ground without difficulty, it must have been continuous. . . . No rain fell on this occasion.

It was unfortunate for this pair that they were walking arm-in-arm and so probably straddling a considerable length of the conducting ironstone vein, and picking up a quite considerable voltage from the current in the ground between the right foot of the one and the left foot of the other.

Fulgurites

When lightning strikes dry rock or sand, the heat of the discharge fuses the material and makes a hole surrounded by a glassy tube. In dry sand these tubes, which are called fulgurites, are sometimes more than 8 feet long. When originally formed their diameter can be as great as 2 inches, but the glassy walls are only about 1/20th inch thick, and they are immediately afterwards compressed by the steam in the ground outside the tube to a smaller ribbed and elliptical shape. In one sand-dune patch of 5,000 acres at Witsands, on the south-eastern border of the

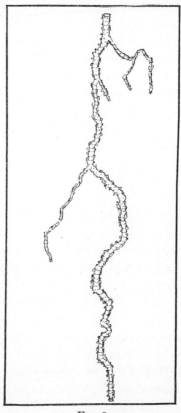

FIG. 8

Kalahari Desert, Lewis estimated that there were not less than 2,000 fulgurites. Since lightning is at the present time very infrequent in this area, some of these tubes must have been formed by lightning-flashes many thousands of years ago.

It is of interest that some of the fulgurites from the Kalahari Desert show fairly definite evidence that the discharge in these cases followed the roots of bushes and plants growing in the sand. Fragments of charcoal have been found associated with them, and one tube had a fine coating of carbon on part of its inside wall. An example is illustrated in fig. 8.

Fulgurites have been made artificially by McEachron, of the General Electric Company in the United States, by passing a high-voltage electric spark into dry sand. The tubular form, however, proved difficult to imitate except with low-current discharges lasting for several seconds, as heavy-current rapid discharges blew the sand away.

The Colours of Lightning

The usual colour of the lightning-flash is an intense white. When viewed through a curtain of rain it is altered, by the action of the drops in filtering-out the blue portion of its spectrum, to a yellow or yellowish-red. Occasionally a very clear rose-pink flash is to be seen, probably associated with the spectrum of hydrogen from raindrops in the path of the discharge. Green flashes have been reported by one authority, but must be very unusual.

A very interesting point arising from studies which have recently been made by Dufay of the spectrum of lightning is that, contrary to expectation, the flashes examined gave very little light in the ultra-violet region. The spectra show strong absorption bands due to ozone, a gas which, as is well known, acts as an absorbing blanket to ultra-violet light and, indeed, prevents dangerous rays of this kind from reaching us from the sun. The amount of ozone blanketing-off the ultra-violet light from the lightning-flash is, however, found to be far in excess of what normally exists in the air at the earth's surface, and it is concluded that it is produced by the streamer processes of the flash itself, presumably in the channel behind the advancing leader.

Mention should also be made of the not uncommon appearance of 'dark' lightning on photographs of flashes. This, which shows itself as black forks and branches where brilliant white ones would have been expected, is a well-known but illusory effect caused by the re-exposure of an exposed photographic emulsion to a bright light. In this case the re-exposure is produced by subsequent strokes of the flash.

The Number and Distribution of Thunderstorms and Lightning-flashes over the World

According to an analysis of meteorological records made by Brookes, the whole world experiences 16,000,000 thunderstorms in the course of a year or, on an average, 44,000 storms a day. Taking one hour as the average duration of each, this means that there are at any one moment 1,800 storms in progress in different parts of the world. From all these storms about 100 lightning-flashes take place every second.

The most thundery region of the earth is the island of Java, where thunder is heard at any one place on about 223 days (61 per cent.) in every year. This percentage is called the isoceraunic level of the place concerned. Other very thundery regions are central Africa (41 per cent. of the year), southern Mexico (39 per cent.), Panama (37 per cent.), Central Brazil (29 per cent.), and Madagascar (26 per cent.). On the other hand, thunder is very rarely heard in Greenland, Iceland, northern Norway, the whole of the Arctic Ocean, and the north coast of North America. Thunder is heard north of the Arctic Circle on about one day in ten years, and over the central Sahara about once a year.

Over most of Europe thunder is heard on the average on about eleven days in the year; near the Alps the figure rises to eighteen days. The frequency of thunderstorms in southern Canada is about the same as in Europe; farther south in the North American Continent the figure rises till it reaches 72 days per year in the states bordering the Gulf of Mexico, and the high value of about 140 days in southern Mexico and Panama. The figure for Johannesburg is 50–60 days in the year.

Thunderstorms are not very frequent over the oceans; exceptions are the areas off the south-east coasts of Brazil and South Africa, and the seas surrounding the islands of the East Indies and Madagascar.

There is very little reliable information as to the number of flashes to ground per square mile per year in different parts of the world. The best estimate for England is six per square mile per annum. The very thundery region of the Transvaal, in South Africa, experiences about twenty ground-flashes per square mile per year.

Thunder

It has been estimated that about three-quarters of the energy of a lightning-flash is spent in the heating-up of the narrow channel of air which it follows. The temperature rises in a few ten-millionths of a second to about 15,000 degrees Centigrade, causing the air in the channel to expand explosively and so create very powerful sound-waves.

Thunder can usually be heard for a distance of about seven miles, though if the air is very still it will carry a distance nearly four times as great. Its characteristic rumbling is due to a variety of factors: the difference in the distances of different portions of the track from the observer, which is also the cause of specially loud crashes when sounds from two different portions at the same distance arrive together; the multiple strokes of the flash; and the echoes of the sound emitted by the channel from different parts of the cloud-base.

Close air-discharges, including many of the flashes which strike aircraft, are often reported to have given rise to little or no thunder. I am inclined to doubt this and to think that in such cases the sound is too weak in intensity to be noticed in the general upset caused by a near discharge. Weak thunder of a special type is to be expected from such discharges, since they often consist entirely, as is shown in Chapter 4, of a series of flickering tongues or streamers, each moving forward a little farther than its predecessor, and since they are not followed by the rapid and brilliant, and noisy, return discharge which produces the characteristic whip-like crack of a flash to ground. Though the series of flickering streamers may be interrupted by more powerful discharges which give proper thunder, they themselves produce a weaker sound, with a pitch between 10,000 and 30,000 cycles per second. This sound, which has been described as that of tearing calico, is often heard from near air-discharges and cloud-flashes, and can sometimes be spotted just before the crack of a flash to ground caused by the return process. This is the noise produced by the stepped leader described in Chapter 4. It is not the same thing as the sharp 'click' which is heard just before the crash of the thunder and which is due to the uprush of streamers of St. Elmo's Fire to meet the down-coming discharge.

The distance from flash to observer is to be found by timing the interval between the lightning and the thunder, each mile corresponding to five seconds of travel of the sound. When the flash is not more than five miles away this method of finding the distance may fail and give the impression of a close flash, when its channel is not really close. The error can arise if part of the flash comes from a charged region in the cloud which is nearly overhead and which produces a discharge which first of all passes more or less horizontally away from the observer and then joins up with the downward channel created previously by another charged region farther off. This case is illustrated in Fig. 15 on p. 86. An observer at A would first hear the thunder from the point B in the cloud, and would wrongly judge that the distance from the point of contact of the flash with the ground was AB instead of the larger value AC.

4

THE LUMINOUS PROCESSES INVOLVED IN THE LIGHTNING-FLASH

'A little information as to fact can at least do no harm.'
C. V. Boys.

In the year 1752, as has been described in Chapter 2, Franklin succeeded in proving that the lightning-flash is in all respects similar to the long electric spark, and produced in the lightning-rod the first practical application of the scientific study of electricity. Since then, though our understanding of the 'electric fluid' and its behaviour has grown enormously and its practical applications have become legion, there has remained until comparatively recently one dark corner, one aspect of its behaviour, about which little more was known than Franklin himself knew. Curiously enough, this was the electric spark itself. Long electric sparks, much longer than Franklin could produce, generated by machines very different from the globes of glass he turned by hand, have, of course, been commonplace for many years. Serving as so-called 'artificial lightning' though without any certainty that they resembled the genuine article particularly closely, they have been employed for a considerable time in the testing of electrical machinery and equipment designed to withstand lightning surges. It is, however, only within the last fifteen years that it has been discovered how the lightning-flash develops and hence how to design test-equipment which correctly simulates it. With this new knowledge has come the explanation of the basic mechanism involved in natural lightning or in man-made sparks, a mechanism which causes such a remarkable change in ordinary insulating air and converts it in a fraction of a second into a white-hot conductor through which electricity can flow nearly as easily as through copper.

The change in the air when a spark passes from one side of

a gap to the other, or when lightning joins cloud and ground for a brilliant instant, cannot take place everywhere along the track of the discharge simultaneously. It must begin at one or other end of the gap, or at both ends, where the electric tension is at its greatest, and then travel across the gap in some manner, creating a conducting channel by breaking down the air as it proceeds. The only way to discover the nature of spark break-down is to devise an instrument which can watch and record this process in action.

What has held up knowledge in this field has been the extremely rapid nature of the process. The gap is crossed, as we now know, at speeds ranging from 60 to 60,000 miles a second, and the break-down process in the longest spark which can be made by man is over and done with in a few millionths of a second. In the case of lightning the gap is much longer, and it takes a longer time to create the conducting channel. Even so, the time taken to cross a mile of air between cloud and ground varies from a hundredth to a hundred-thousandth of a second.

To make an instrument to record the movement of so rapid a process in so short a period of time would seem a very difficult task, but such an instrument was designed in the year 1902 by one of the most ingenious of all experimenters, Sir Charles Boys, who invented for this purpose the special lightning camera which bears his name.

The Boys Camera
'Boys will be Boys'—SIR RICHARD PAGET.

The principle on which the Boys camera is based is best understood by considering what would be found if we could photograph a lightning-flash on a cinema camera which took a million pictures every second. Since the flash must start somewhere and ultimately create a conducting channel a mile or more long, the successive pictures on this imaginary cine-camera should show luminous tentacles, or *streamers*, moving from cloud to ground, or from ground to cloud, or from the air between to both ground and cloud. The study of these streamers would give us the information we wanted. Such a cine-camera could perhaps be made, but it would be very elaborate, and Boys obtained the same result in a much simpler way. If the lens of an ordinary camera could be moved very rapidly in front of its film and the picture of the lightning-flash so obtained could be compared with another of the same flash taken by a camera with a fixed lens, the two photographs would be the same only if the lightning-flash or the electric spark were a simultaneous affair along the whole length of its channel. If part of the flash occurs later than the rest, the movement of the lens in the first case will shift the recorded picture taken by it. To illustrate this, Fig. 9a shows a lightning-stroke photographed by an ordinary camera with a fixed lens. This is repeated in dotted form in the figures which follow. Fig. 9b shows what the same stroke might look like when recorded on a camera in which the lens was moving rapidly from left to right while the luminous streamer moved downwards from cloud to ground. Fig. 9c shows the stroke moving upwards from ground to cloud, and Fig. 9d the same stroke starting in the air between cloud and ground and developing both upwards and downwards. It will be clear that the motion of the lens has shifted or distorted the track of the discharge from the form it would have taken on an ordinary camera with fixed lens. If the discharge process moves downwards there is a shift to the right in its lower, and later, portions, and if it moves upwards it is the upper portions which are so shifted. The difference between the shifts at any two points along the channel ($AA'-BB'$ in Fig. 9c) divided by the speed of the lens, gives the time taken by the streamer to pass from one point to the other. In this way, by measuring the shifts at prominent bends or branches and making a simple calculation, a complete 'timetable' for the movement of the streamer could be drawn up.

The distance of the flash from the camera can be found by timing the interval between the lightning and the subsequent thunder. With this information, and knowing the focal length of the camera lens, we can determine the distance, in two dimensions, from one prominent point to another. We can

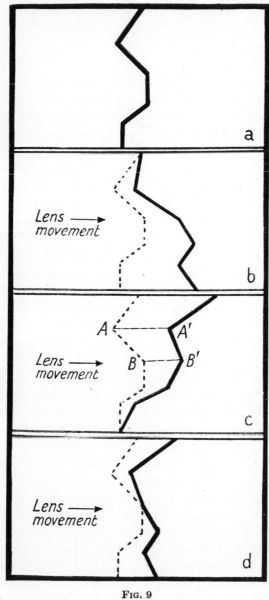

FIG. 9

F

then make use of the time-table to find the speed of movement of the streamer from point to point along the channel.

It was on this principle that Boys had the brilliant idea of basing an instrument that could measure the speed and record the movement of lightning-streamers. Before he could do this he had to decide whether it had any chance of succeeding; whether, in fact, a camera of this kind would be likely to give shifts which were large enough to measure. To answer this we need a little arithmetic. It is not practicable to move the lens of the camera at very much more than thirty miles an hour, or approximately 500 inches per second. It is also not practicable to measure a distortion or shift on the plate or film which is smaller than 1/2,000 of an inch. The smallest shift which could be relied on therefore corresponds to $1/2,000 \times 1/500$ seconds, which is one-millionth of a second, conveniently called one *micro-second*. We must next estimate how far a lightning-streamer can be expected to move in this time. To take the most unfavourable case, suppose that the streamer moves with the speed of light, the fastest speed at which any moving body or process *can* move. This is 186,000 miles per second. In one micro-second it will travel 0·186 miles, or 327 yards. It should therefore be possible, with a camera working on this principle, to produce a time-table for the movement of a lightning-process every 327 yards, even if the streamer-process moved with the speed of light. Actually it would be reasonable to expect, as subsequent experience has shown to be the case, that few, if any, of the streamer-processes would move as fast as the speed of light, so that the position was even more favourable to the prospects of the camera.

A few troubles remained which were not easy to solve. The first was the problem of how to move a lens at thirty miles an hour (at night, of course, when there would be no fogging of the film) and have it always in front of the film for the five minutes or so during which it is necessary to wait for a lightning-flash. Boys's solution of this was to give the lens a rotational and not a linear motion, by revolving it in a circle in front of the film. The second was how, in practice, to compare two separate prints of the same flash, taken on separate cameras, one with a fixed and the other with a moving lens, to an accuracy of 1/2,000 inch. Accidental errors in lining up the two prints and the effects of mechanical vibration during the

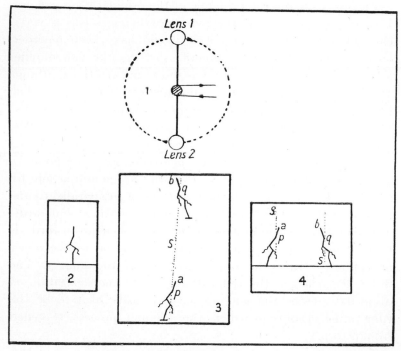

FIG. 10

instant of photography could easily give rise to spurious shifts greater than this. Boys solved the problem by not using a fixed-lens camera at all, but making the moving-lens camera two cameras in one, with two revolving lenses mounted at opposite ends of a diameter of a revolving disk, as shown in Fig. 10 and Plate III. The film of the double camera then records two separate photographs of each part of the discharge, taken through lenses which are always moving in opposite direc-tions; for when one is vertically above the other, the top lens is moving momentarily to the right while the bottom lens is moving to the left; and when they are horizontal, one is momentarily moving downwards and the other is moving upwards. These lenses produce equal and opposite shifts of the streamer pictures, which, incidentally, doubles the accuracy of measurement.

Fig. 10 (1) shows the principle of the original Boys camera. If a discharge occurs at the moment when one lens is vertically above the other, and if it would have been recorded on an ordinary fixed-lens camera as at (2), the two moving lenses will give a double picture as shown at (3) if the lightning-streamer process were moving downwards at this stage. The later, bottom, portion of the luminous channel would be displaced to the right by the upper lens and to the left by the lower one. For an accurate measurement of these shifts, a line *psq* is drawn on the print to connect corresponding points *p* and *q*, and the two portions of the print are mounted side by side as in Fig. 10 (4), with their sections of *psq* parallel to one another and the two directions of lens movement outwards. The fact that the luminous process travelled downwards is then at once shown by the greater separation of the lower as compared with the upper portions of the images. The difference between the separation *pq* and the separation *ab* divided by twice the lens velocity is easily seen to be the time interval during which the original process travelled from *a* to *p*.

The reader may well have noticed the assumption in this explanation that the stroke occurs at the moment when the lenses are at the top and bottom of their circular path and momentarily moving nearly horizontally. Though this is the most convenient position for discussion of the principle involved, it can easily be seen by trial that the shift, though no longer horizontal, will be the same for any position of the lenses. When they are momentarily moving vertically, the vertical portions of the streamer-channel will be lengthened by that lens which is moving in the same direction as the streamer and shortened by the other lens, and these changes in length can be measured.

The lenses have no shutters, and the camera in its original

form can be used only at night and away from the lights of towns. It is set up on a stand and faced towards an approaching storm, the lens caps removed, the plate exposed, and the lenses rotated by turning a large wheel fitted with a belt which drives a pulley on the disk carrying the lenses. As soon as a flash has been recorded the plate is changed for a fresh one.

The speed of rotation is most easily checked and kept constant in field-work by turning the lenses at such a speed as to be just below a critical resonance vibration of the camera body. In a lightning observatory of the kind later built at the Bernard Price Institute for Geophysical Research in Johannesburg, many refinements in technique can be introduced, including electric motor-drive and more elaborate forms of camera, some of which will be described later. The essential features of the discharge-process in the lightning-flash have, however, been discovered by cameras very similar to that first made by Boys in 1902. The original instrument, which is now in the Science Museum in London, is shown in Plate III, in the hands of its inventor.

Boys himself never secured a satisfactory picture of lightning, though he tried to do so for thirty years. In 1933 the author decided to make a serious attempt to obtain results by this method. With the aid of a team of workers in the Transvaal and the support of the South African Institute of Electrical Engineers, three Boys cameras of improved design were constructed, and these were operated by the team for several years. Conditions were more favourable than they had been for Boys in England, for summer thunderstorms are very frequent near Johannesburg. Even so, it was by no means easy to obtain the number of really good pictures needed to establish the whole history of the development of a lightning-flash. The cameras, and the electrical equipment mentioned in the next chapter, had to be taken at short notice and at any hour of the night into the country away from city lights, and got ready at vantage-points selected so as to be well in front of the approaching storm. This was necessary because rain and hail falling from the cloud blurs the pictures of the lightning-channel and makes it difficult to make accurate measurements of the distortional shifts.

After we had obtained our first results and had learned something about the more brilliant streamer-processes, we found that it was necessary to concentrate on recording very near flashes, for only then could we succeed in photographing some important processes which give out less light than the others. These near records were difficult to obtain, but we were fortunate in having in our team Mr. H. Collens, an engineer who devoted most of his spare time to the task, and brought to it the same skill and experience which had previously made him renowned as a fisher of man-eating sharks and an expert in the art of capturing crocodiles alive. The members of the team spent several fruitless nights in rain and hail for each successful result, but in the course of four years we secured about 150 good Boys camera records of flashes to ground, comprising in all some six hundred of the separate lightning strokes described on p. 41. Later work in our lightning observatory has produced many more.

General Results obtained from Photographic Studies of the Discharge

A typical photograph of a lightning-flash, taken by Mr. H. Collens, is shown in the upper part of Plate IV. This flash was made up of eight separate strokes at various intervals of time, and its total duration was about 0·4 seconds. Since one revolution of the lenses occupied only 0·04 seconds, the whole picture involved ten revolutions, and the strokes were not recorded in the order of their occurrence. Their order was obtained from a subsidiary camera with a single slow-moving rotating lens which, with an ordinary fixed-lens camera for general reference, completed the equipment used. In Plate IV the strokes are not lettered in their proper sequence, stroke f being actually the first of the series. The central inset shows the flash as photographed on an ordinary camera with a fixed lens.

The lower picture of Plate IV shows the two records of a single stroke (d of the series above) mounted for the purpose of measuring the distortions produced by lens motion. It will be seen that since the lenses were moving outwards, in the direction of the arrows, the first event in this particular stroke must have been that for which the separation of corresponding points on the two pictures is the smallest. This is the point X (or X') where the discharge-process first left the cloud. After this the separation increases as we move our measuring instrument down the channel until we reach Y (or Y'), where the streamer was very close to the ground. The figure also shows that the lightning-process was a double one. The first part, XY, was succeeded by a return process along the same path from Y to Z, for ZZ' is greater than YY'. The difference between the two is, however, much less than between YY' and XX', proving that the return process was very much faster than the original downward movement. The figure further indicates that the return process is much brighter than the earlier downward movement.

This picture is typical of all strokes in a normal flash of lightning to ground. Each stroke is double, consisting of a faintly luminous *leader* streamer passing from cloud to ground, with the main emission of light from a region just behind its advancing tip (Fig. 11*a*) and followed by a brilliant *return* streamer passing from ground to cloud along the path formed by the leader but in the reverse direction (Fig. 11*b*). These illustrations show successive 'snapshots' of the leader and the return streamers. The leader is, however, much slower than the return streamer, and so while the snapshots in (*a*) are drawn at intervals of three thousandths of a second, those in (*b*) are at intervals a hundred times shorter—thirty millionths of a second.

When, as is usual, the discharge consists of a number of separate strokes or partial discharges, each of these has its own leader and return streamer. (Where Plate IV does not show such double streamers it is because the leaders are too faint to be reproduced and only the more brilliant return streamers can be seen.)

The leaders usually travel at speeds from one thousandth to

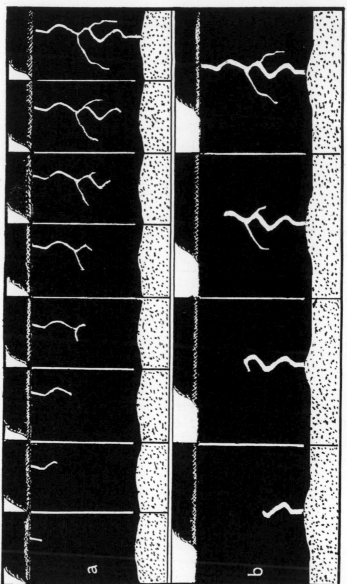

FIG. 11

PLATE III

C. V. Boys

Photograph by Lafayette

Sir Charles Boys with his first lightning-camera

PLATE IV

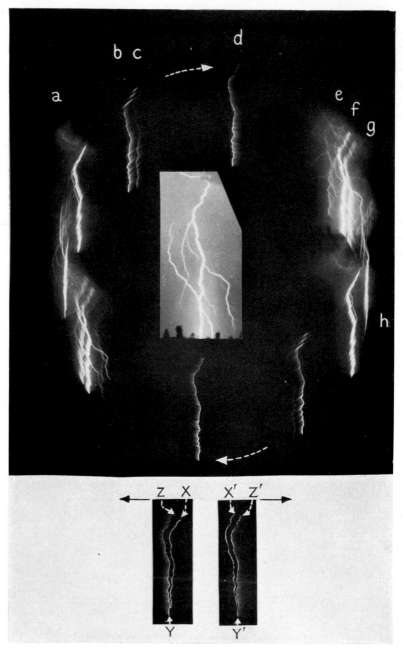

Boys-camera picture of a lightning-flash, with fixed picture and pictures of stroke 'd' mounted for measurement

PLATE V

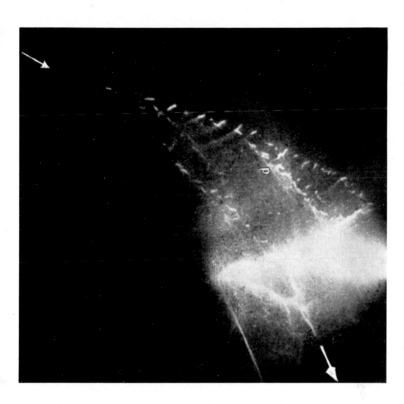

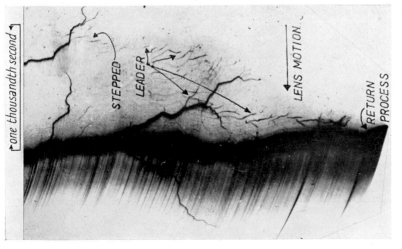

Stepped leaders to first strokes

PLATE VI

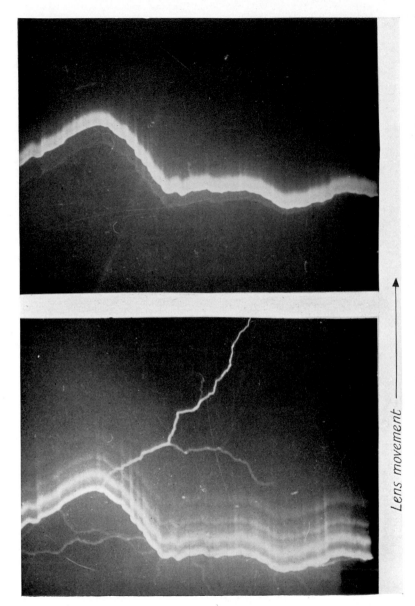

Lens movement ⟶

Flash of two strokes photographed on a fast-moving camera in daylight

one hundredth of that of light, that is, from 186 miles per second to 1,860 miles per second.

The return streamers are much faster than the leaders and travel at speeds which are at first about one tenth of that of light; as they pass upwards they slow down somewhat, and they may enter the cloud at about one hundredth of the speed of light.

The leader in the first stroke of a discharge to ground is hard to photograph unless the flash is near, but it is of special interest, for it creates the track which is followed by all subsequent processes. The camera shows that it progresses differently from the leaders in the subsequent strokes. Instead of moving steadily downwards it advances in a series of steps, each about fifty yards long, and pauses for about fifty microseconds after each such step, behaving as if it were exhausted and needed time to recuperate. After a pause, the process is repeated with a new step downwards, the new movement involving a rejuvenation of the part of the channel already created by the streamer, which gives out a burst of light along its whole length, though not as brightly as does the new step. Each step is made in a different direction from the previous one, and it is at the start of a new step that the streamer sometimes forms forks or branches, whereupon the leader continually divides along different paths, each itself involving a series of steps.

Two examples of Boys camera pictures of stepped leaders are shown in Plate V. The left-hand picture, shown as a positive print, was taken by Dr. D. J. Malan at a distance of less than a mile from the flash. The arrows on the pictures show the direction of movement of the camera lens in each case. The earliest events lie to the right; they consist of the stepped streamers already described, very bright at the ends but giving out light all the way from cloud-base to their tips. Between each step there is a pause which may last from 30 to 100 microseconds. Branches can be seen in various places. The much more brilliant return streamer tracks are over-exposed because the flashes were very near.

The stepped-leader process is found to be an essential preliminary in every flash to ground, and explains several peculiarities of the discharge. In the first place, it is evident that the tortuous zigzag nature of the channel arises from the hesitant nature of this first process, which has to make use of every accidental variation in the condition of the air in order to reach the ground at all. Secondly, the point which is finally struck by the flash is determined only when the branching stepped leader has got fairly close to the ground, often only in the last hundred yards of its movement. And finally, the observation that practically all lightning-discharges fork or branch in a downward direction is explained by the fact that it is a downward-moving leader streamer which produces them.

Since Boys camera pictures are not easy to interpret, Fig. 12 has been prepared so as to show the course of a stepped leader streamer as it would be recorded by a cine-camera taking 1,000 pictures a second. The steps are shown as full black lines and the fainter streamers connecting them to the cloud as dotted lines.

It will be seen that the progress of the leader and its branches is apparently quite haphazard; purely local conditions in the air determine which branches will develop and which will not. Even at a late stage in its progress it is not possible to tell which of the branches will be the one which finally makes contact with the ground and so form the main channel of the discharge. In the last picture but one it is still an open question whether it will be *a* or *b* which hits the ground first. The final picture shows that circumstances connected with the ground surface, perhaps a tree or a building, gave *a* the advantage, so that it developed more rapidly in the final stages than *b*. At an earlier stage, when the leader was only two-thirds of the way down, an accidental variation in the air might have made branch *c* develop faster than the others and so might have caused the flash to strike the ground half a mile or more from where it did. The figure also shows that branch *b* was very close to the ground when the return streamer started from the end

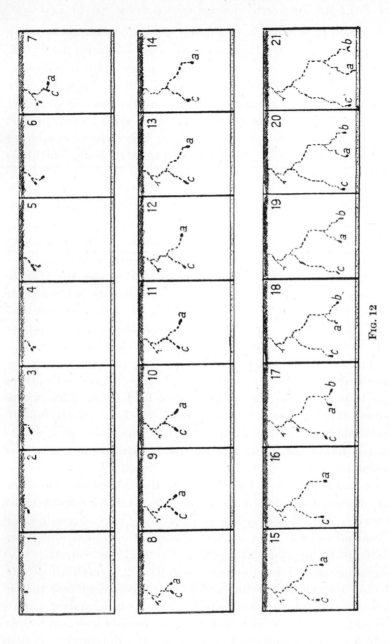

Fig. 12

of branch *a*. Sometimes it is found that two branches are both so close to the ground that a return streamer starts from both, and the flash 'hits the ground' in two places, but such double-hitting, an example of which is quoted on p. 40, more often arises from another cause—the failure of the channel to persist in a conducting state between strokes. If the time interval between strokes is exceptionally long, it is not uncommon for the next stroke to be preceded, as far as its lower portion is concerned, by a new stepped leader to a new target on the ground.

Leaders to strokes other than the first of the series do not, however, usually show any steps or pauses at all but pass continuously down the original channel without forming branches. As is shown by the examples in Plate IV, the light emitted by these leaders is most intense at the tip and for something like fifty yards behind it, becoming feeble farther back. If the eye could see such a leader, it would look like a brilliant dart or arrow passing down the channel, and for this reason such leader streamers are called *dart* leaders.

The return streamer process has been said to start at the moment the leader hits the ground. In fact, it does not wait for the leader, but joins it with a burst of brilliant St. Elmo's Fire about ten yards above the ground. It then travels rapidly upwards, and as it goes up the main trunk also passes outwards along the branches formed by the leader, which it illuminates once more. An actual time-table for a return streamer is shown in Fig. 13, where the figures give the time in micro-seconds taken to reach each point. The accuracy of measurement is not always as good as one micro-second, since some parts of the record are less clearly defined and more difficult to measure than others. It will be seen that the streamer passed up the main trunk and entered the cloud 26 micro-seconds after it started from the ground, and that it fell off in speed as it went up the trunk, taking only 4 micro-seconds to reach point *a*, but 6 micro-seconds to travel from *a* to *b*, and 16 micro-seconds from *b* to *c*. It will be seen also that after it had disappeared from view inside the cloud it was still

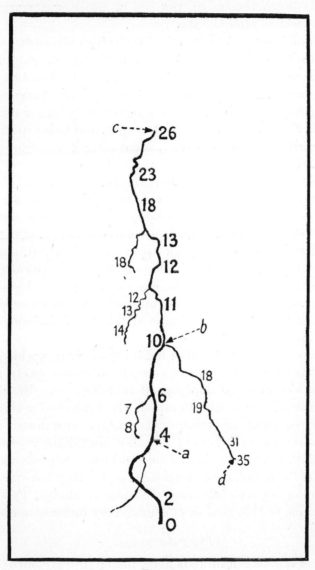

FIG. 13

passing down branch *bd*, the end of which was reached 35 micro-seconds after the start.

The rapidity and brilliance of the return streamer indicate that it is the main carrier of current in the lightning-discharge, as is confirmed by the electrical measurements described in the next chapter. The arrival of the return streamer at each branch is signalized by an increase in the light emitted along its whole length. Similar fluctuations in the light, and hence in the current carried by this streamer, occur after it has entered the cloud. The detailed study of these fluctuations is of great interest and some practical importance.

Although it reaches the cloud very quickly, the streamer often continues to keep the channel luminous for a considerable time afterwards. After it has entered the cloud it 'mops up' electrical charges, which are widely dispersed, and this mopping-up process means a flow of electric current along the channel. The duration of the continuing current due to this process, as indicated by the light given out and confirmed by actual measurements on flashes striking high buildings, can sometimes exceed half a second.

It has been suggested that lightning-discharges which have abnormally long continuing currents are more likely to set fire to forests or to unprotected buildings than those with return strokes of shorter duration. The evidence for this view is derived from laboratory experiments with long electric sparks carrying currents of the same magnitude as those in lightning. These have been found to form artificial fulgurites or to set fire to inflammable material only if they have a longish continuing current following the main discharge. Field corroboration of this view is, of course, very difficult to obtain.

The Pilot Streamer

There is good reason to believe, though the argument is too involved to be given here, that the stepped leader process is not the whole mechanism of the first leader. It is, in fact, superimposed on another very slow streamer, which gives out too little light to be photographed. This streamer, which I have called the *pilot streamer*, is the real pioneer of the lightning-flash, but it cannot go the whole way from cloud to ground unless it is periodically caught up and helped on its way by the step streamers. Owing to its slowness it would not be expected to give out much light, and it has so far escaped the eye of any camera. During the pauses between the steps the pilot streamer forges steadily ahead with but little emission of light, like the tortoise of Aesop's fable, to be caught up at the end of each pause by the faster and brighter hare. Evidence for this pilot streamer is largely indirect, but its electrical effects are quite clear and will be mentioned in the next chapter.

Air-discharges and Cloud Flashes

When air-discharges, which do not reach the ground, are recorded on moving-lens cameras, they are found to consist in the main of stepped-leader processes only, with occasional bright dart leaders following up along channels already formed. Since they make no contact with the ground, they show no return streamers.

Flashes within the cloud cannot be examined by the photographic method, but their electrical effects indicate that they also consist of stepped- and dart-leader processes only.

Discharges to very High Buildings

The general picture which has now been given of the stages in the development of a flash to ground in South Africa has been found to hold good in other parts of the world, with one interesting exception discovered by McEachron and McMorris, of the General Electric Company in the United States, who have studied lightning-discharges to the Empire State Building by means of Boys cameras. In the case of this high structure, which extends about half-way from the earth to the base of many thunder-clouds over New York, the development processes are not always of the kind found elsewhere. While about 25 per cent. of first strokes and all subsequent strokes show the normal downward leader and upward return stroke, in 75 per cent. of first strokes the stepped leader is found to travel *upwards* from the Empire State Building to the cloud. The steps are similar to those shown by normal downward leaders, but the leader process is not followed by a return stroke from the cloud. Instead, the establishment by the leader of a conducting channel from earth to cloud is succeeded by a continuous illumination of this channel and a continuing current which has on occasion been found to last for nearly a second.

These upward stepped streamers from a high tower are an extreme manifestation of point discharge (St. Elmo's Fire). Ordinarily the electric tension at the ground is not great enough to turn the glow at the top of an elevated conductor into a moving streamer unless a leader has come down from the cloud and is within fifty feet of the rod; but these observations show that when the conductor is as high as that on the Empire State Building it can often do so.

Developments of the Boys Camera

When one comes to study fine details of the leader and other processes in the lightning-discharge, the original form of the Boys camera has certain defects, arising chiefly from the circular track followed by its lenses. This restricts the total length of plate or film surface available for the record to about twelve inches, and a good deal of overlapping occurs in the photographed tracks of the separate strokes and their leaders. The time taken by a stepped leader to pass from cloud to ground is sometimes so long that its steps are spread over most of the circle and are difficult to locate and study amongst the other portions of the flash, especially the intense return streamers.

Boys himself designed a form of the camera with two fixed lenses and a moving film which to some extent avoids this difficulty and gives its records on a length of thirty inches of film, with the distortional shifts always in the horizontal direction. We have successfully used a camera of this type, but have found it to suffer from limitations in light-gathering power and to present difficulties in rapid changing of film. It is of great importance in this work to be able to change film quickly so as to make full use of a good storm.

In our more recent work in South Africa we have gone back to the principle outlined on p. 64, in which a single moving-lens picture is compared with a fixed-lens picture. In these later studies we have not required information about the time-table of the return streamer, but have been interested in the leader process and in the continuing luminosity which follows after the return streamer has reached the cloud. Since these processes occupy times very much longer than the 50 micro-seconds or so taken by the return streamer to reach the cloud, it is possible without appreciable error to treat the return streamer picture as if it had been taken on an ordinary fixed-lens camera, and to measure the distortional shifts in the leader streamer record with reference to it. For this purpose, there-fore, I have used only one lens and that a fixed one, while the film, four feet long, is carried in a special mounting on the surface of a large drum revolved at high speed by an electric motor.

In our most recent camera, designed by Dr. D. J. Malan and Mr. R. D. Linton and shown in Fig. 14, the recording film E, 44 in. long and 35 mm. wide, is fixed in guides on the inside of a circular box forming the camera body. Immediately after a picture has been taken the film can be wound on a spool (by a mechanism not shown in the diagram) and a fresh length quickly exposed. In the figure the film has been cut away to show the rotating arrangements inside it. The light from the flash enters at D and is caught by a moving prism, A; it then passes through a Wollaston prism, B, which is turned by a pair of gear-wheels at half the angular velocity of A, and through the rotating lens, C, which throws the image of the flash on the film. The Wollaston prism, B, is necessary to prevent the image from turning as the main prism, A, moves round. A, B, and C are revolved by the shaft, F, which is turned by an electric motor. The optical system has been designed to have high light-gathering properties.

With this camera, as with its predecessor, we have been able to arrange that the lightning-flash takes its own photograph. At D, in front of the aperture of the prism A, is mounted a quick-acting shutter which can be opened in 1/500th of a second by a rod pulled by an electromagnet. Each of the

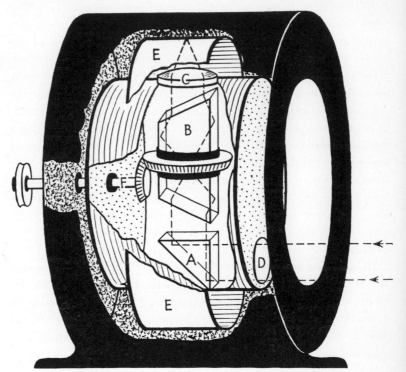

FIG. 14

sudden steps in the first leader-process, as will be explained in Chapter 8, sends out a wireless-wave, and the whole series of steps produces a series of waves whose frequency is set by the most usual pause-time between steps, 50 micro-seconds, and so is about 20,000 cycles per second. By tuning a special wireless-receiver to this frequency and by arranging that the output from the receiver operates a trigger-valve which can energize the electromagnet connected to the shutter, the waves from the first few steps of the leader open the shutter. The delay involved by this mechanism is so small that film is exposed well before the first leader has reached the ground. It is a simple matter to arrange for the shutter to close itself a second later.

This system has the great advantage that it enables the camera to be operated in the daytime. Ordinarily, to open a large-aperture lens for a whole second in daylight means ruining the film by fogging. But, since the optical system is moving round, the length of exposed 'film' in this case is 44 inches instead of the $1\frac{1}{2}$ inches covered by the field of the lens if it had not been moving, and the actual exposure to daylight is not 1 second but 1/30 second. With a suitable film and under the overcast conditions prevailing at the time lightning photographs are taken, the fogging is not serious. An example of such a record taken in daylight by the author, and showing a good dart leader on the second stroke, is given in Plate IV. The stepped leader to the first stroke is too faint to be reproduced. The two strokes occurred at an interval of 0·019 seconds and were photographed 14·3 inches apart on the film. The light in the channel after the first return streamer-process shows violent fluctuations associated with the mopping-up process in the cloud, as described on p. 78.

These daylight cameras have made it possible to obtain a very large number of pictures of lightning, because there are so many more storms by day than by night. By cutting down the amount of night-work involved they have also much reduced the difficulties of securing information and have, incidentally, made life much less of a trial for the investigators and their long-suffering families.

5

THE ELECTRICAL PROCESSES IN THE LIGHTNING-DISCHARGE

'First let me talk with this philosopher.
What is the cause of thunder?'
King Lear.

THE sharp eyes of the cameras described in Chapter 4 have revealed the four main processes in the lightning-discharge— the pilot, the stepped, the dart, and the return streamers—and have given us a great deal of information about them based upon the light which they send out. But these processes are themselves primarily electrical in nature; the light they emit is a secondary effect arising from the electrical changes in the air through which the streamers pass. We now inquire what is the nature of the fundamental processes in the discharge.

The problem is not an easy one, for the processes are very complicated. It is, however, interesting and important not only in itself but also because its solution contributes to the fuller understanding of what happens in the much shorter pre-liminaries to the spark-discharge. To solve it, the information given by photographic studies of the discharge must be supple-mented by electrical studies made, if possible, at the same time. The whole of this information has to be combined with the great, though still incomplete, mass of knowledge obtained from laboratory studies of the passage of electricity through gases.

The Charges on the Thunder-cloud

Whenever electricity is produced, and by whatever means it is produced, equal and opposite quantities of positive and negative charge must be generated. An electrical generator, whether it be a dynamo, or a piece of glass rubbed with a silk handkerchief, or a thunder-cloud, does its work by separating these equal and opposite charges from one another. In the dynamo they go to the positive and negative terminals of the machine, in the rubbing of glass to the glass and the handkerchief respectively, and in the thunder-cloud to the top and bottom of the cloud.

Investigators of thunder-clouds are now in agreement that in whatever part of the world thunder-clouds are in action the great majority of them, perhaps all, carry a positive charge on their towering tops and a negative charge on their dark, threatening bases.[1] The way in which the clouds generate these charges and place them a mile or more vertically above each other by vertical currents of air will be discussed in Chapter 7. Here we need simply accept the fact of separation and the conclusions of many experimenters that the lower portion of an active thunder-cloud almost always carries a negative charge.

The Reason for Separate Strokes

As has been described on p. 41, the most frequent number of separate strokes in a single flash is three, though many more are found in flashes from big clouds, and a small cloud may often give only one. An explanation of the way in which separate strokes originate was given by me in 1937. It is that a single thunder-cloud usually consists of a number of separate 'generators' of electricity, being divided into a number of separate active regions in which the necessary upward winds and other conditions for the generation of charge exist. The existence of these separate regions of up- and down-draught has recently been established by meteorological investigations made from aircraft specially flown through thunderstorms. They are known as cells, and are further described in Chapter 7. In a small cloud there may be only one of them; in a large one, as shown diagrammatically in Fig. 15, there may be many.

A flash to ground begins with the downward movement of the pilot and stepped leaders from that negatively charged region in the base[1] of the cloud (marked 1 in the figure) which is by chance most favourably situated for a leader to start, because it has developed to the breakdown point more quickly

---

[1] Here, as elsewhere, 'base' means the lower portion of the cloud, within which some negatively charged centres may be higher than others, their height depending on their history.

than the others. After this first region has been discharged by the leader and return streamer process described in Chapter 5, the second charged region reaches the ground by making a connexion within the cloud with the top of the conducting channel formed by the first region. Once a junction is made between region 2 and the top of the original channel, a dart

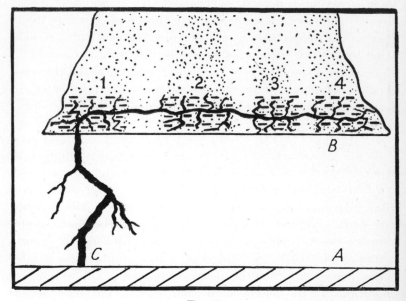

Fig. 15

leader–return streamer process gives the second stroke and completes the discharge of the second region. The remaining charged regions, if they are able to send out the necessary junction streamers, repeat the process and give the further strokes in the series which make up the discharge. The figure shows the final stage at which regions 2, 3, and 4 have all successively linked up with the channel formed by region 1. The negative charges shown in regions 1, 2, and 3 of the diagram have in reality disappeared in the first three strokes to ground at the time depicted in the diagram.

From this explanation of the cause of separate strokes we can proceed to estimate the average distance between the charged regions in the cloud. It should be the product of the most frequent interval of time between strokes, 3/100 of a second, and the most frequent velocity of the stepped leader-process making the junction, which is 130 miles a second. The answer of 3·9 miles checks reasonably well with what is known from more recent meteorological observations of thunder-cloud cells. The distances between the centres of five such cells in one cloud recently measured in Florida averaged 4·5 miles.

The Mechanism of Streamer Movement

Some of the return streamers in the lightning-flash carry electric currents which measurements show to be as large as 200,000 amperes. For currents of this magnitude to be transmitted through a channel of air not more than six inches in diameter a very drastic change must have taken place, because the air is normally an excellent, though not perfect, insulator.

The very small power of ordinary air to conduct electricity arises from the fact that a small fraction of its molecules have become electrically charged, or ionized, by losing or gaining an electron. The air around us normally contains about 10,000 ions in every cubic cm., an infinitesimal number compared with the millions upon millions of neutral molecules, but enough to make it a feeble conductor, or a not-perfect insulator —whichever way you care to look at it.

These ions are created from ordinary molecules of oxygen or nitrogen by the impact of fast-moving particles from the cosmic rays which come from outer space, and of fast-moving particles sent out by atoms of radium emanation (and their descendants), which enter the air from the soil. A good many of the ionizing particles are fast electrons, moving at sufficient speed to knock other electrons out of the molecules with which they collide. It is, however, only when they have reached a certain critical speed that electrons can do this; below this speed they merely bump the molecules without ionizing them, and finally end their careers by slowing down sufficiently to be caught by a molecule, which is then converted into a negative ion.

These are the normal natural processes of ionization;

something very different can take place in the powerful electric fields of thunder-clouds. For in these fields a single electron, produced by any accidental process, can be accelerated by its repulsion from the negative pole of the cloud and its attraction either by the positive pole at the top of the cloud or by the positive induced charge on the ground, getting faster and faster until it reaches or even surpasses the critical speed for ionization.

When it reaches the critical speed a new process begins. The original electron creates another by ionization, and since this is also in an accelerating electric field it also becomes an ionizing electron. So the process multiplies itself by a chain reaction until from the original single electron a vast avalanche of electrons is created. One electron in a field sufficiently strong to cause it and all its progeny to reach the ionizing speed could in this way create twenty-four million others in travelling a distance of one centimetre, and 2·8 million million million in travelling an inch. The electron avalanche would clearly reach an impossible size were it not for a moderating influence which checks its growth by a means which will be described in the next section.

The Leader-process

The process of electron avalanche formation is the method by which the leader streamer advances. Given a thunder-cloud field which is sufficient to enable an electron to accelerate up to the critical ionizing speed, and given also a single electron— easily produced from natural sources—the avalanche can start and a downward-moving leader can be born. Its speed would be not much more than the critical value, for the leader must be expected to move as soon as conditions are right for it to break down the air in front of it. The critical ionizing speed is known from theory to be about 90 miles a second, and the Boys camera results give 62 miles a second for the minimum velocity of first pilot streamers passing into virgin air. This general agreement is itself a convincing argument for the electron avalanche explanation of the leader-process, and

provided the clue on which the further interpretation of the
electrical phenomena of the lightning-flash is based.

Fig. 16 represents the early stages in the start of an electron

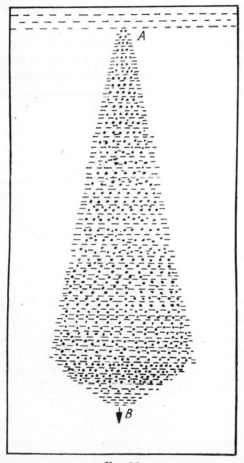

FIG. 16

avalanche streamer. The negative cloud-charge whose repelling
field provides the driving-force, and which starts the first
electron of the chain at *A*, is at the top of the figure. The fastest
of the avalanche electrons have reached *B*, so that the streamer
extends from *A* to *B*. The electrons are indicated by — marks
and the positively charged molecules which they leave behind

are represented by black dots. In order to show these in the diagram the avalanche has been made much wider than it would actually be. For a length AB of two inches, the bottom and broader end of the avalanche would actually be only 1/50th of an inch across. It will be clear that the advancing electrons are not only pushed forward by the repulsive field of the cloud but are also pulled back by the attraction of the positively charged molecules from which they have been broken off. The two forces are opposite in nature, and the nearer positive ions in this way put a brake on the development of the avalanche, and so check its growth that it does not get out of control; it is able to move forward, but not much more. The electrons at the tip of the leader streamer will for this reason travel on at a speed not very much greater than the minimum ionizing speed. Local differences in the physical condition of the air they are penetrating will have a powerful influence on the direction they take and will in this way give rise to twists and turns in the streamer-path.

The conditions in the channel behind the advancing avalanche-tip of the streamer are complicated by processes other than the ionization we have mentioned. In moving forward into virgin air the electrons at B will have numerous bumping or non-ionizing collisions with neutral molecules, collisions which will give to the molecules a great deal of energy. Sometimes these bumps make the molecules move faster, which has the effect of raising the air in the channel behind the tip to a very high temperature. Sometimes, however, the collision disturbs the electrical structure of the molecule, and it goes over into what is called an excited state. A very short time afterwards the molecule returns to normal, and in doing so gives out light. Within about fifty yards of the invisible avalanche-tip of a leader streamer, the molecules which have been so rudely jostled a short time previously as to become excited, are returning to normal and are making the channel luminous. Farther back than this, what little light is emitted comes from those few molecules which have been abnormally late in recovering from excitation. In the case of the pilot streamer the intensity of the light is too small to be recorded photo-graphically. The same excitation-process is at work in leader streamers and is the reason why they are recorded photo-graphically as luminous darts, or steps—bright javelins about fifty yards long, with darkening tails behind them. The light emitted from behind the tip of the streamer may be of some help in assisting the tip to move forward by ionizing a few of the molecules ahead of the tip.

So far we have described an electron avalanche advancing into very feebly ionized virgin air and so we have dealt only with the case of the slow-moving pilot streamer of the first leader. Subsequent leaders advance along the somewhat cooled but still heavily ionized channel formed by previous strokes. Their progress is therefore much assisted by the fact that extra electrons already exist in considerable numbers *ahead* of the advancing streamer. Electron avalanches are continually form-ing well in front of the tip of the streamer, with the interesting consequence that the streamer as a whole moves faster than the individual electrons themselves are moving. In much the same way a rumour can travel faster from end to end of a crowd of people in a queue than it would if it were simply repeated from one to another, since it is heard by people some distance away from the speaker and can be repeated by them to others farther away. It is for this reason that all streamer-processes along previously ionized channels travel at speeds so very much faster than that of the initial pilot streamer, which has to make its own ionization by avalanches starting from its tip.

The Junction of the Leader with the Ground

As the leader travels down, it drastically alters the air it penetrates. Every cubic cm. of its channel contains not the usual ten thousand electrified ions but about one thousand million million; the channel formed by it becomes equivalent to a good conductor, branching out like a many-tongued metal connexion from the cloud into the air below. On the surface of the conducting channel is carried a considerable part, often more than half, of the charge originally on the cloud-base. The downward rush of the leader is thus a process in which a good deal of the electricity on the cloud is lowered much closer to the ground than it was before. Four stages in this process are illustrated in Fig. 17.

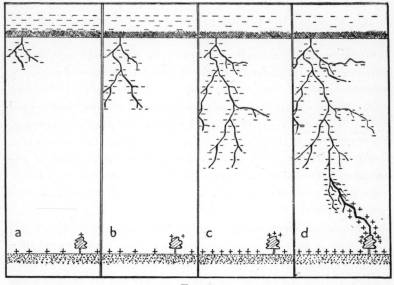

FIG. 17

The lowering of the cloud-charge produces an exceptionally strong electric field between the leader and the earth. As illustrated in Fig. 17d this field ultimately causes a positive streamer of St. Elmo's Fire to spring out of the ground and rush upwards to effect a junction with the leader. It has been estimated that if there are no projecting trees or buildings below the leader, this junction-point will be about fifteen feet above the ground.

If the ground below the leader has a tall projecting object like a tree or building on it, the positive streamer will start earlier and the junction-point with the leader will be higher up. A lightning-conductor on a building can produce a streamer which will make contact with the leader about fifty feet above the building. It is in this ability to produce a longer junction streamer than any other projection, such as a chimney, in its neighbourhood that the protective value of the lightning-conductor lies.

Exceptionally tall conductors, like the Empire State Building in New York, go perhaps too far in this respect. By sending up positive streamers which can travel the whole distance to the cloud, they often actually invite flashes of lightning to occur to them. A lightning-rod of ordinary height does not invite discharges; it simply collects them when the leader-process brings them dangerously near the building which is to be protected.

Though it has long been considered essential to provide the conductor with one or more sharp points, as Franklin originally proposed, these points can have little, if any, effect on the length of the streamer and hence on the protection afforded by the rod. Laboratory experiments with short sparks do show that streamers are more easily produced from sharp points than from blunt rods, but on the scale which prevails in Nature the blunt top of any rod is equivalent to a needle-point and no advantage is to be expected from sharpening it.

The Return Stroke

The upward positive streamer from the earth is the beginning of the return stroke, and, in view of the conditions provided for it, it is not surprising that it is extremely fast and violent. Its progress is maintained by electron avalanche-processes acting 'in reverse'; in this case, as illustrated in Fig. 18, the electrons in front of the advancing tip are pulled in, not pushed away. As shown in the figure these forward electrons move downwards, producing avalanches as before, ionizing, heating, and exciting the molecules in their path. On account of the heavy pre-existing ionization (produced by the leader) in front of the upward-moving positively charged tip of the streamer, it moves extremely fast, and is responsible for the heaviest current and the most brilliant emission of light in the stroke. As it moves upwards it passes the electricity on the leader and its branches to the ground, and finally discharges the cloud

itself. Its progress is most vigorous at its start when the ionization in front of it is most intense, because it has been formed

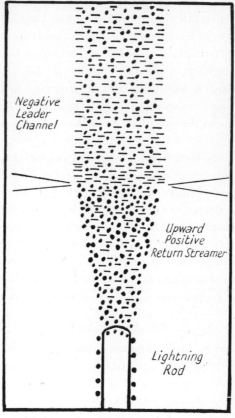

Fig. 18

just a few micro-seconds previously by the leader and no
appreciable re-combination of the ions has yet occurred.

The Stepped Leader Streamer

In describing the progress of the first pilot leader streamer
as an electron avalanche with a heavily ionized channel behind
it, one point was omitted in order to avoid over-burdening the
account with too much detail. All is not well with the ionized
channel behind the avalanche. Although it is ionized, some of

the ions quickly re-combine and tend to reduce its conductivity to such an extent that the electrons in front do not after a time obtain the necessary push to proceed on their way. When this hold-up occurs, a new fast streamer is generated in the cloud which passes from the cloud down the original channel until it catches up with the advancing leader-tip. This step streamer moves along a pre-ionized channel and is therefore very rapid and gives out enough light to be photographed, becoming especially bright when it reaches the last portion of its course, which has previously only been traced by the pilot streamer. The evidence from both camera and electrical studies indicates that the failure of the channel behind the pilot avalanche to support its further progress occurs with remarkable regularity after the tip of the pilot streamer has moved forward a distance of from 30 to 90 yards.

Electric Field Studies

Electric charges, like the poles of a magnet, show an effect at a distance; this effect can be measured and is called their 'electric field'. Important information about the electrical processes in the discharge has been obtained by studying the electric fields of thunder-clouds while lightning-flashes are taking place. The most recent investigations make use of the cathode-ray oscillograph—the instrument employed to display television pictures—to record changes of field taking place in a millionth of a second or less. From these a great deal can be deduced about the strength and distribution of the charges producing the field.

Fig. 19 illustrates some of the results of an investigation of this kind. The upper strip shows in diagrammatic form the various streamer-processes in the case of three strokes of a lightning-flash recorded on a fast camera whose film is moving from right to left. For ease of interpretation the flash is supposed to be a straight vertical one with a single branch. The lower strip shows the corresponding electric field and its changes as they would be observed at a distance of three miles from the discharge.

The reader will see that as the first leader streamer travels downwards at *a*, the electric field at *b* becomes more and more negative until junction is made with the earth at the moment marked 1 and the return streamer starts upwards. Then follows the rapid passage to earth of the negative charge on the leader and on the first-charged cloud region, with a corresponding rapid disappearance of the negative fields due to them. The

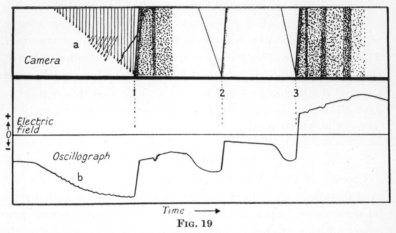

FIG. 19

process repeats itself in subsequent strokes from other regions in the cloud. The final result is to create a strong positive field, due to the positive charge on the top of the cloud, which charge has not taken part in the flash.

Fig. 19 shows three strokes, whose return-processes begin at the times marked 1, 2, and 3. The camera record depicted in the upper strip shows a continuing luminosity after the return stroke in the case of the first and last strokes. The electrical effect of these is a continuation of the positive change in the electric field, though at a much slower rate than in the return portion of the stroke.

During this continuing luminosity of the first and third strokes, the diagram shows some fluctuations in the light from the channel of the flash of the kind which have already been described on p. 78. The corresponding electrical changes are the little hook-shaped kinks shown in the lower record.

At this distance of three miles from the flash the first leader steps show themselves as the minor sudden kinks on the electrical field-change record which are illustrated at *b* in the figure. Farther away from the storm, as will be discussed in Chapter 8 and as illustrated in Fig. 28, they are more significant in relation to the other field-changes. They can, in fact, be picked up as electrical changes many thousands of miles away from the flash which caused them. It is by means of them that the device described on p. 82 opens the shutter of the camera to enable a lightning-flash to take its own picture.

Studies of Direct Strokes to Conductors

Many direct studies have been made of the magnitudes and the variations with time of the currents carried at the 'business ends' of lightning-strokes. The information is required by manufacturers of electrical machinery both in order to devise suitable test equipment—artificial lightning—to ensure that insulators, transformers, and other component parts of electric power distribution systems shall be able to withstand damage by lightning, and also to improve protective devices. The lightning-strokes which have been studied directly in this way have been collected by moored balloons, by long rods placed on mountain-tops, by conductors mounted on high buildings like the Empire State, and by electric power-lines and their supporting towers, and have been measured with ingenious recording instruments connected to the bottom ends of these collectors.

As would be expected, the heaviest currents flow during the first few micro-seconds of the return stroke, during and just after the moment when the cloud and earth have joined. The current rises in from $1\frac{1}{2}$ to 10 micro-seconds to a very high peak value, and thereafter falls, coming down to half its peak value in from 25 to 100 micro-seconds. It may continue to flow at a low value for a considerable time afterwards.

The biggest currents observed have been in the neighbourhood of 200,000 amperes, but the most frequent value is much lower—30,000 amperes. About 10 per cent. of all strokes give peak currents exceeding 60,000 amperes and about 10 per cent. of all strokes give currents less than 20,000 amperes.

The Electric Spark

Observation of the properties of the electric spark two hundred years ago led men to surmise that the lightning-flash was a phenomenon of the same nature as the spark but on a vaster scale, and led Franklin to prove that this was indeed the case. It is pleasant to record that the studies of the lightning-discharge outlined in this and the previous chapter have in their turn been able to throw a good deal of light on the processes taking place in the formation of the shorter electric spark.

In the case of a spark between a negatively charged point and a positively charged, or earthed, flat plate, the resemblance to the lightning-flash is very close. A negative streamer, travelling at about the same speed as a first leader, proceeds from the point until it is met by a short positive junction streamer from the plate, whereupon a return streamer passes rapidly back along the channel.

In the case of a positively charged point and a negative plate the leader, like many of those from the Empire State Building, is a positive streamer. When a spark passes between two points or balls, leader streamers travel out from both electrodes, but the positive streamer is the quickest and bridges most of the gap before the negative streamer is able to join it.

Some Quantities

The potential difference between the upper and lower poles of the cloud and between the lower pole and the ground just before a flash takes place is between a hundred million and a thousand million volts.

After a flash the cloud-charges are replenished by a charging mechanism, described in Chapter 7, which supplies a current of about 4 amperes. Left to itself without hindrance this mechanism would re-charge the cloud in some 5 seconds; actually, owing to leakage losses, the full re-charging process takes 20 seconds or more, depending upon circumstances which vary a great deal from one cloud to another.

The most frequent value for the quantity of electricity discharged in a complete flash is 20 coulombs. Values as high as 160 coulombs have on occasion been observed. The quantity discharged in a single stroke is usually from 2 to 10 coulombs.

The most frequent peak value for the current in the return stroke is 30,000 amperes; the highest value observed is 200,000 amperes.

The average value of the energy spent in a flash to ground is five thousand million calories; most of this is converted into heat and sound. A cloud giving one flash every twenty seconds is dissipating electrical energy in the form of lightning at an average rate of a million continuous kilowatts.

6

PROTECTION AGAINST LIGHTNING

'Clear proofs are afforded by trustworthy experiments rather than by the probable guesses and opinions of ordinary professors and philosophers.'

WILLIAM GILBERT, 1600.

The Effectiveness of Lightning-conductors

THE revolutionary effect of the introduction of the lightning-rod in protecting churches and public buildings has been described in the first two chapters of this book. The effectiveness of the rod in the case of houses and barns is still not fully appreciated, and it has been estimated that not more than one in five of the buildings in the United States which are liable to damage by lightning are protected in any manner against it. This indifference on the part of the owners of these buildings, says a report by the United States Bureau of Standards (Technologic Paper No. 56, 1915, by O. S. Peters), may be traced to several causes, not the least of which is the impression left by unscrupulous lightning-rod agents of sixty or seventy years ago, who prospered greatly at the expense of a credulous public.

Rods of every description were then erected at excessive cost to the purchaser and in most cases without much regard for the rules that should be followed in their erection. The object was to make a great showing with a minimum of material and labour; to accomplish this the conductors in many instances were discontinued a few inches below the surface of the ground. . . . Hundreds of people were swindled in this manner and found themselves in possession of what might have been a very useful device, if properly installed, but which soon came to be regarded as more or less useless by their unfortunate owners except as scrap metal, and as a joke by those of their acquaintances who had escaped the wiles of the agent.

The best evidence for the positive value of Franklin's rod comes from the reports of fire-insurance officials in the United States, who have paid particular attention to the moneys they have had to pay out for fire losses due to lightning, and have compared their payments on protected and unprotected buildings. In the State of Iowa, for example, over a five-year period (1919 to 1924) lightning caused 924 fires, of which 874, or 95 per cent., occurred in buildings which were not 'rodded', and only 50, or 5 per cent., occurred in rodded structures. The difference cannot be attributed to a smaller number of rodded buildings; in the rural districts, where most of the fires took place, the numbers of rodded and unrodded buildings were about equal. Since some of the rods may have been faulty, the evidence given by these and similar figures from other States shows quite conclusively that a lightning-rod provides a very considerable protection.

It is estimated that an unrodded farm building with a thatched roof, or one containing inflammable straw or hay, is about fifty times as liable to catch fire from a lightning-flash as a rodded building of the same kind. Many insurance companies in the United States either refuse to insure unprotected farm buildings, or insure only for an added premium to cover the additional risk of fire from lightning.

Similar evidence comes from other countries; a statistical report by Dr. van Gulik to the Netherlands Academy of Science shows that in the case of houses roofed with tiles or slate the danger of fire by lightning is reduced by a factor of seven if the house is protected with a lightning-rod.

In spite of these figures, lightning still takes a considerable toll of unprotected property in the country from which the rod came. The United States National Board of Fire Underwriters placed it in 1921 in the sixth place of causes of fire, and estimated that it was responsible for an annual direct loss of somewhere between twelve and fifteen million dollars. The indirect loss, due to interference with business and farming, was considerably more.

Factors to be Considered in Providing Lightning-protection

In determining what is the need for lightning-protection in specific cases one must take into account a number of factors. The first is, of course, the frequency and severity of thunderstorms in the area concerned; in areas where lightning is very infrequent, only buildings which are of special importance or are inflammable need be protected. The next is the position of the building itself; an isolated house on a hill-top is very much more likely to be struck than one in a valley, especially if the valley is a deep one. In closely built-up towns, where there are high electric standards and overhead wires and trees, the hazard is not so great as in the open country, but even there the danger to human lives needs consideration. There are in the cities many large buildings which have been built of reinforced concrete without proper attention to the connecting together (bonding) of the steel structure; a lightning-discharge to such a building, if it is not provided with a lightning-rod system, may injure or kill some of the occupants. Special consideration should be given to structures such as the chimneys and buildings of water-pumping plants on which communities depend for their health and general amenities. In the case of large public buildings or monuments the provision of lightning-conductors could with advantage be considered at the time they are designed, so that the conductors do not spoil the appearance of the structure.

A completely safe protective system, which is very expensive and which can be justified only in the case of buildings which contain explosive or inflammable chemicals, is an all-metal structure completely bonded and well earthed at at least one point. An approximation to this degree of safety is to enclose the building in an earthed network of copper ribbon, as was done to the town hall of Brussels in 1865 by Melsens. The Eiffel Tower, which is in effect such a 'Faraday cage', has frequently been struck by lightning without any ill effects to visitors inside it.

Each case for lightning-protection must be considered in the light of these factors and, in general, the policy should be to provide rather more protection than seems absolutely necessary. To see what this requirement is we must next consider what protection a single rod will provide and what is involved in correctly setting up a protective system.

The Degree of Protection afforded by a Single Rod

The sole function of a lightning-rod is to attract to itself a flash which would otherwise hit some other part of the building. It accomplishes this by virtue of its height and its good connexion with the ground. These enable it to produce an upwardly directed positive streamer which, because it is of greater length than any other in the neighbourhood, joins up with the negative leader streamer coming down from the cloud, and so joins the discharge from the cloud to the earth through the conductor itself, without damage to the rest of the building. The usual length of the streamer rising from the rod is somewhere between fifteen and thirty yards.

There has been much discussion, ever since the first lightning-conductors were put up, as to the radius of protection afforded by a rod. If by this is meant the radius of *complete* protection against all flashes, it is very difficult to give an answer to the question. From time to time there are bound to be leader streamers either coming down to ground at an angle very much inclined from the vertical or with much less charge than usual and therefore less power to pull off a long positive streamer from a rod. These weak or inclined leader streamers will sometimes be able to 'get under the guard' of a lightning-rod and to hit portions of the building which would in most other cases be sheltered from damage. But they are comparatively rare, and if we exclude them we may talk of the radius over which the rod will give reasonably complete protection, which means that perhaps only one in a hundred flashes will be able to get in under the guard of the rod and hit within the protected area. For the ordinary householder, even in a bad lightning area, this is good protection, for it will probably cover his lifetime and that of his children. For a dynamite factory, on the other hand, it may not be considered good enough.

Recent statistical and theoretical studies show that a lightning-rod will provide this type of protection against all flashes which fall within a 45-degree cone, like a bell-tent, whose top is the top of the conductor and whose base is a circle of radius equal to the height of the conductor above the ground. This is

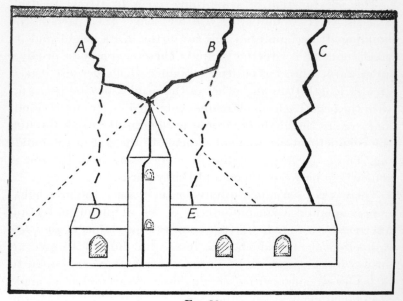

FIG. 20

illustrated in Fig. 20, in which flashes *A* and *B*, which would normally have hit the roof of the church at *D* and *E*, pass to the conductor, while flash *C*, directed towards a part of the roof outside the protected area, will strike it because its path falls outside the cone. Unless the roof is of metal and earthed, additional conductors with elevation rods should be mounted on it, as shown in Fig. 21, so that the whole building is sheltered within their 45-degree cones.

It has from time to time been suggested that the 'bell-tent' or 45-degree cone of protection just described is too conservative and gives an underestimate of the zone protected by a lightning-rod, and that the radius of the base of the protective cone could be taken to be at least double the height of the rod above the ground. The arguments for this increased radius are not based on statistics (which, indeed, show that even the 45-degree cone does not give 100 per cent. protection) but upon some fairly early tests with so-called artificial lightning in the

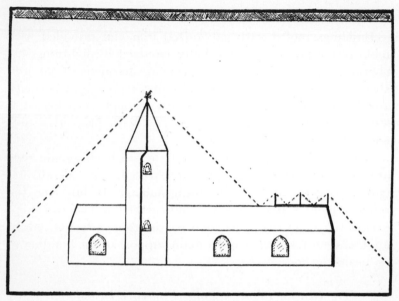

FIG. 21

form of laboratory sparks and model houses to scale. Apart from doubts which exist as to whether such scaled-down tests have much real meaning, the sparks used did not correctly simulate the lightning-flash, for they did not cross the gap between the artificial cloud and the model ground by negative leader-processes. Unless, therefore, only a moderate degree of protection is required of a lightning-rod, it should be considered to offer protection only over the 45-degree cone and then only for the great majority of flashes.

Ironically enough, one of the earliest lightning-rods, erected in 1772 on Franklin's advice on the powder magazine at Purfleet (p. 26), failed to protect the building against a lightning-discharge within the 45-degree cone, much to the benefit of Benjamin Wilson, who believed its failure to be due to its point. The flash which came in under the guard of the rod was, as would be expected from the explanation given, a very weak one, and did little damage beyond dislodging a few bricks.

Metal-roofed and Reinforced-concrete Buildings

Buildings roofed with galvanized iron and provided with metal drain-pipes are not usually troubled by lightning discharges even in areas where storms are frequent, if the iron sheets are in good contact with one another (preferably bonded), and the drain-pipes suitably earthed; though even here it is a wise precaution to fit the chimneys with protective rods connected to the roof itself.

Reinforced-concrete buildings, if the steel reinforcing rods are properly bonded together and earthed, are generally regarded as very safe from lightning damage. If, however, the reinforcement is not so bonded and earthed, a flash can cause destructive cracks as the current passes from one set of rods to another—for instance, from a main support of the building to its beams or floors.

The General Principles of a Protective Installation

The essential parts of a lightning-conductor system are three in number. The first is a system of rods projecting above the roof or chimneys of the building to form the tops of the 45-degree cones necessary to protect it. These are called *elevation rods*. The provision of sharp points at their ends will not affect their performance in any way, though it will do no harm.

The second is an arrangement of copper or iron (strip or rod) conductors connecting the elevation rods together and joining them to one or more *down conductors* which end in the ground connexions. These conductors should be of a thickness sufficient to carry the heavy current of the discharge for the short period of its duration without getting very hot. There is no need for them to be insulated from the roof or walls of the building unless the roof is of thatch, when they should be kept well away from it. They should have no sharp bends, for the rapid rush of current in the return portion of the stroke will cause the discharge to take some other path and give rise to side-flashes if bends impede its progress.

A celebrated case of the failure of a lightning-protective system owing to a sharp bend occurred in 1829, when a discharge caused the explosion of the supposedly well-protected powder magazine at Bayonne in France. The conductor had been bent through a right angle two feet from the ground, and was then carried horizontally on wooden posts for thirty-three feet to a trench, where it was buried in the earth. The discharge refused to take this path and struck the roof of the magazine instead.

The other obvious point to be watched about the conductors is that the joints between different sections are well made and do not work loose or break with the passage of time; but the possibility of this defect should not be regarded in too serious a light, since the discharge is quite capable of jumping across bad joints or even small breaks in the conductors.

There has been a good deal of controversy about the type of metal to be used in lightning-conductors. The first conductors were made of iron, and when properly put up they gave good results. A well-known case of damage due to an inadequate conductor occurred in 1839, when the Hôtel des Invalides in Paris was damaged by a lightning-discharge because the iron-wire cable used as a conductor was not able to carry the current. Later, when copper became more easily obtainable, it supplanted iron to large extent, and has since remained more or less generally in favour because it has a greater resistance to corrosion. Heavily galvanized iron, however, resists corrosion nearly as well. In 1892 Sir Oliver Lodge advocated the use of iron for conductors on the grounds that its higher resistance would damp down oscillations in the discharge current which might lead to 'side-flashes' from the conductor to the building. We now know that such oscillations do not occur, and this particular argument in favour of iron falls away.

The third component of a lightning-protection system is the *ground* or *earth connexion*. This is vital to the successful performance of the system, since a poor ground connexion means that the discharge, after being attracted to the rod and down-conductors, is unable to pass easily between the ground and

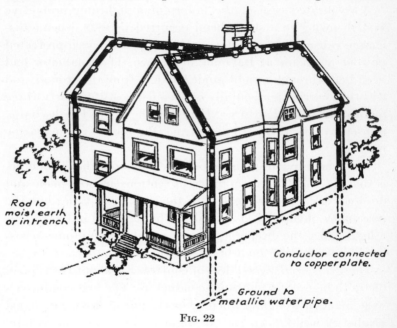

Rod to
moist earth
or in trench

Conductor connected
to copper plate.

Ground to
metallic water pipe.

FIG. 22

(by courtesy of the National Fire Protection Association, U.S.A.)

the cloud and may jump to some alternative path, with consequent damage to the building. If it is at all possible the ground connexion, whether in the form of a straight rod or a pipe or a large plate of metal, should be sufficiently deep for it to lie in moist earth. When the ground is very dry or rocky and this is not feasible, then it is best either to connect the conductor to a water-pipe in its immediate neighbourhood (a gas-pipe connexion is obviously dangerous) or else to set up a system of radial strips of copper or galvanized iron in trenches round the building. The practice of putting salt round an earth connexion to keep it damp is a bad one, since it leads to rapid corrosion. The electrical resistance of a ground connexion should be as low as possible, but in practice figures not exceeding 10 ohms are considered acceptable. When the ground is so dry as to make the resistance above this figure, the special steps already described have to be taken to improve the position by making a number of such earth connexions or by using a water-pipe.

Full technical details for the correct setting up of a lightning-protection installation are given in codes of practice published by the standardizing organizations of most countries. In the case of a valuable or an important building it is desirable to entrust the planning and installation of the protective system to an expert in this field or to an engineer who has a copy of the recommended code of practice. For smaller buildings, and particularly for farm properties, a valuable simplified code has been issued by the Department of Agriculture of the United States (Farmers' Bulletin No. 1512), which describes in detail some useful cheap methods of protection. In Fig. 22 is shown the form of lightning-protection usually recommended for a large house in a bad lightning area. The diagram illustrates three possible types of earth connexion.

The Effect of Discharge to a Lightning-rod upon nearby Metal Objects

Many cases of damage to buildings which have apparently been properly fitted with lightning-protection have been found to have been due to the presence in close proximity to the rod of a mass of metal which was neither connected to the rod nor earthed. Amongst these have been sheet-metal roofs, gutters, metal roof-ornaments, and water-pipes. When the heavy current from the discharge passes along the rod it causes it to assume momentarily an electrical potential which may exceed half a million volts, and this can produce side-discharges to nearby metal objects which may cause damage. All such objects, if they are within six feet of the conductor, should be earthed and joined to the conductor itself; but it is better to place the conductor at least six feet away from them, and also from electric light- and telephone-wires and gas-pipes. The large metal tanks used for the storage of petrol and oil require

special attention in this connexion. On 23 July 1905 a large
tank of oil at Humble, Texas, was set on fire by lightning,
starting a fire which spread rapidly through the whole oil-
field and burned for three days. Twelve men were killed and
over two million barrels of oil were destroyed. In 1926 millions
of dollars' worth of oil and equipment were lost from the same
cause in California, where, as a rule, there are practically no
thunderstorms except those made in Hollywood.

What may be a serious cause of lightning-fires is the practice
recently adopted in South Africa of thatching dwelling houses
with wire loops instead of twine. In some cases metal bars are
used to support the thatch in place of the customary wooden
ones. Metal objects of this kind are not only targets for side-
flashes from the lightning-rod, they can also provide sparks by
induction, the metal loops and bars acting as the secondary
windings of a transformer of which the conductor is the
primary. In bad lightning areas, thatched houses of the old
wood-and-twine type, though vulnerable, have not nearly as
high a casualty rate as this newer type. Where, as not infrequently happens, the lightning-rod is actually passed through
the thatch, it is a positive danger and not a protection at all.

Protective Masts and Trees

In view of what has been said it will be clear that a good
method of protecting a thatched building from lightning
damage would be to erect more than six feet from it one or
more large metal masts, of piping or similar material, so
arranged that the whole of the building lay inside the 45-
degree cones of the mast system. Provided the masts are
properly earth-connected and the joints in them are electrically
sound, this system, which is illustrated in Fig. 23, should be
very satisfactory, and perhaps the most suitable one for
houses in bad lightning areas. It has been used for many
years at the large explosives factory at Modderfontein near
Johannesburg.

It is often thought that high trees in the immediate neighbourhood of a house give similar safety to it, but there have

been a good many cases where trees have proved a danger rather than a protection. Although its elevated top may attract a lightning leader, the trunk and the roots of a tree often offer a very poor path to ground for the discharge, and side-flashes may pass to metal portions of a nearby building, which provide a better path. Indeed, it is generally recommended that trees

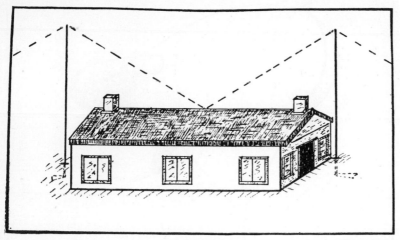

Fig. 23

of historical or other importance be provided with lightning-conductors of the same kind as used for buildings. An important case is that of an isolated tree which may be used for shelter by people or by cattle during a storm. There will be far less danger from side-flashes if it has a conductor attached to it and if it is surrounded by a wooden fence to keep shelterers a few feet away from its trunk. Without such protection an isolated tree is dangerous shelter from lightning.

Captive Balloons

An interesting case of the application of the lightning-rod arose during the recent war in the protection of hydrogen-filled barrage balloons in Great Britain. After some preliminary and fruitless attempts to protect these captive balloons against lightning by insulating them from the ground, they were provided with metallized conducting envelopes, and lightning-conductors, as shown in Fig. 24, were mounted on them.

Under comparable conditions the unprotected balloons were then found to be three to four times as likely to be set on fire

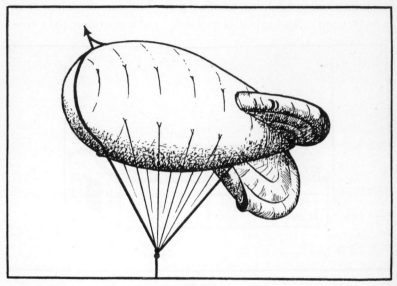

FIG. 24

by lightning as the protected ones. At least twenty-one balloons protected in this way were known to have survived direct lightning-strokes. The crew operating the balloon-cable and its winding-gear stood on an earthed metal sheet connected to the winch. When the balloon was struck they must have been at a potential of about a million volts with reference to the earth, but those who went through this experience reported only a slight tingling sensation.

Protection of Human Beings and Livestock

The number of persons killed by lightning in the United States every year is about 500. About 1,300 are injured from the same cause. Ninety per cent. of these casualties occur in rural districts amongst the farming population and other persons whose occupations keep them out of doors during stormy weather. It has been stated that 52 per cent. of all lightning fatalities occur in the open, 38 per cent. in houses and barns, and 10 per cent. under trees. The most dangerous places out of doors are small sheds, isolated trees, wire fences, and hill-tops; the safest ones are depressions in the ground, deep valleys, the foot of steep cliffs, or a grove of trees.

A number of lightning fatalities have occurred in swimming-baths. Some of these have been caused by the current from nearby flashes flowing through the water, others by the break-down of electrical power fittings in the neighbourhood, with the result that the power supply has passed through the bath.

Indoors in a properly protected building there is little lightning hazard, though telephones should not be used during a storm, radio sets should have their aerials earthed, and water-taps be avoided. When unprotected houses are struck people can be injured or killed in almost every conceivable place in the house, but in general the most dangerous places are near telephones, taps, and chimneys, or in the neighbourhood of stoves and other large masses of metal.

The injuries produced by lightning vary from very serious burns, and in some cases tearing of the flesh, to mild cases of electric shock. Many persons apparently killed by a near flash have been restored to life by the quick application of artificial respiration and other general treatment for electric shock. When the body receives the full force of a lightning-flash it is doubtful whether life can be restored to it; in many such cases the heat of the discharge produces such a rapid generation of steam that the boots and clothing of the victim are stripped off and thrown some distance away. There have, however, been some occasions when the lightning-flash has cured instead of killing people, by providing the equivalent of modern electric-shock treatment. In 1782, for example, the priest attached to the household of the Duke of Kent was cured of 'paralysis' by being struck by lightning.

The loss of livestock by lightning in parts of the United States has been sufficient to cause a good deal of concern to farmers, and in many cases precautions have been taken to minimize it. The greater portion of the loss is caused by cattle drifting against wire fences during thunderstorms and being killed by electric shock. The shock may not be due to a direct stroke, near or distant, to the fence, but to the sudden release of induced charges on the fence wire. To obviate this it is often considered worth while not only to earth the wire fence at intervals of fifty to a hundred yards, the distance depending on the degree of dampness of the soil, but also to break the metallic continuity of the fence by inserting in it pieces of wood or other insulating material two feet long every three hundred yards.

Electric Power and Telephone Lines

The development of electric-grid systems covering large areas of the country and leading off with feeder lines to isolated houses and farms has produced a new problem in protection, for lightning is the chief cause of interruption of the service provided by these power lines, as it is of interruption in long-distance telephone and telegraph systems. To ensure continuity of service, many power systems link up additional generators to their lines when thunderstorms are approaching.

The most frequent trouble is that the discharge strikes the line and causes a powerful spark to pass from it to ground by way of the insulators. The insulators may in this way be punctured and cease to perform their function, because the ordinary voltage of the line is now sufficient to continue the spark as an electric arc, or 'flash-over', after the lightning-discharge is finished. Generally, however, the flash-over either ceases with the end of the discharge which caused it or can be removed by switching off the power supply automatically for a few seconds. Less frequent but more troublesome in its effects is the discharge which, without always striking the line directly, causes a 'surge' of current to flow along it to the equipment at its end, where damage of a costly nature may be caused. In the case of telephone lines and low-voltage power lines the terminal equipment can be adequately protected by fitting a suitable type of safety spark-gap to enable the surge to jump harmlessly to earth before it can reach the equipment. A protective gap of this kind is a sort of electrical safety-valve, and the lines entering an important telephone-exchange or 'repeater' station are often fitted with a series of such gaps set to 'blow-off' at progressively lower voltages as the terminal is approached.

For high-voltage power lines such simple safety gaps are, however, not suitable, because the spark may continue as a flash-over in the gap after the surge is over. More complex types of arrestor gaps have therefore been developed, in which the line is separated from earth by a special material which is normally an insulator, but which breaks down and becomes a conductor when the voltage across it exceeds a certain safe value. The material reverts to its normal insulating function when this excess voltage has gone. One of the most successful of these devices is made of porcelain, whose interstices are packed with conducting particles of carborundum. When the surge arrives at one end of such a device it creates in it a multitude of tiny sparks which pass internally from one end to the other; as soon as it has been disposed of, the sparks cease. By distributing the sparks over so many little gaps the material does not shatter even when subjected to the heaviest discharges.

Surges of this kind can be due to two causes, direct lightning-strokes to the power or telephone lines, and induced effects, when the charge induced on the line by an overhead thunder-cloud, like the charge on the rod in Fig. 2, is released (as a result of a discharge in the cloud or to ground) and flows in both directions along the line, seeking its way to earth. Induced surges have a much lower voltage than those due to direct strokes, and so cause more trouble on low-voltage power lines and telephone lines than on high-voltage lines.

A considerable measure of protection against both the direct and the induced effects of lightning can be obtained by placing one or more earth-wires above the power or telephone wires themselves. Such earth- or guard-wires are commonly to be seen stretching from tower to tower of electric grid systems. Cases where they fail to give protection are almost always found to have arisen from a direct stroke which, after striking the earth-wire, has passed to ground by way of the tower and encountered too high a ground-resistance at its foot. The tower and earth-wire then acquire a high voltage with respect to earth, and a flash-over can take place from the tower to the power line by way of the insulators, some of which may be damaged as a result. Electrical power engineers have therefore to direct attention to the proper earthing of their towers, not always an easy matter in dry or rocky areas.

In the case of an important power line from a station generating 100,000 kilowatts at Witbank, in the Transvaal, very significant results were obtained by improving the 'footing' resistance between tower and earth. The line consists of two circuits of 132 kilovolts, suspended from cross-beams on the same set of towers. Originally the tower-footing resistance averaged 14 ohms over the whole line, and was much higher than this at certain towers which were prone to lightning damage. During this period both lines were put out of service by flashes on about eight occasions each year. This figure was cut down to less than two occasions a year after special efforts had been made to reduce the average tower-footing resistance to 6·4 ohms and to allow it nowhere to exceed 8 ohms. With other devices, including guard-wires and automatic line-tripping relays, the lines have been free for the last ten years from any complete interruption of service due to lightning.

As an early example of the effectiveness of such precautionary measures in a bad lightning area, Shipley has quoted the case of a power line (22 k.v.) in Nigeria which, when first brought into use without protection, experienced thirty-two shut-downs due to lightning in one year, totalling thirty hours of service-time lost. After it had been fitted with puncture-proof insulators, and an earthed guard-wire, together with special arrestors at three critical points, the shut-downs fell to about four per year and the annual loss of service-time to about one hour.

The electrical power-supplies to the gold-mines of the Witwatersrand in the Transvaal, because of the magnitude and extent of the grid system, are exposed to very severe lightning hazards. They are carried on routes which include nineteen 80,000-volt lines, on tall towers; these high-voltage lines alone cover 1,052 miles of an area where summer thunderstorms are frequent and where the ground is often dry and rocky. Much effort has been required to reduce the loss of supply caused by lightning-flashes to the lines.

In the summer of 1947–8 the high-voltage lines suffered no less than 101 lightning flash-overs on their insulators. The Victoria Falls and Transvaal Power Company, which operated the service until July 1948, has in the course of its many years of experience fitted all the protective devices mentioned in the preceding pages, and has particularly relied upon automatic switches which, if a flash-over occurs, break the power-supply to the affected line for three seconds and then return it to service. Their experience has shown that this interval is sufficiently long to extinguish the power-arc which follows a lightning flash-over unless serious damage has been caused by it. On each of the 101 occasions mentioned above, the lines were automatically tripped and returned to service in this way. On ninety-six occasions all was well, the fault had been cleared; on five the line was still unserviceable. Restoration of service on one of these occasions took four hours, on the remaining four a total of forty-three minutes.

The total aggregate running-time of the nineteen lines during the year July 1947 to July 1948 was 166,440 hours; in spite of 101 lightning faults the total number of service-hours lost from lightning was only 4 hours 43 minutes.

7

THE ELECTRIFICATION OF
THUNDER-CLOUDS

'Behold, slow-settling o'er the lurid grove
Unusual darkness broods; and growing gains
The full possession of the sky, surcharged
With wrathful vapour . . .
                    and in yon baleful cloud,
A reddening gloom, a magazine of fate,
Ferment.'

JAMES THOMSON: *The Seasons.*

THE thunder-cloud, or cumulo-nimbus, is described by meteoro-logists as a great mass rising in the form of mountains or towers or an anvil, generally having a veil or screen of fibrous texture at its top, and at its base a dense layer of dark, shapeless cloud with ragged edges from which rain or snow or hail may fall.

Thunder-clouds usually develop from large masses or long banks of cauliflower-headed cumulus clouds, which are lower in height and smaller. Such a group of clouds amalgamates into one large mass with an extensive upward development of towering heads and the formation of the characteristic threatening base.

Measured from the ground, the tops of these clouds usually reach to a height of from seven to ten miles, and their bases are from $\frac{1}{2}$ mile to $2\frac{1}{2}$ miles high, depending upon local conditions. The area covered by the base is very variable; a front of 10 miles and a depth of 5 to 10 miles is not uncommon, and still larger clouds are frequently seen. If there is much hail in the cloud its lower portion takes on a greenish sheen.

The lifetime of a thunder-cloud is usually from one to four hours. It contains inside it a very large mass of water in a variety of forms—hailstones, ice particles or snowflakes, large drops and tiny droplets. In the part of the cloud above the temperature at which water freezes many of the droplets are not frozen to ice but exist as water in a super-cooled form.

These super-cooled droplets are a troublesome hazard to air-craft, for they are responsible for 'icing' conditions—the formation of ice from them on the wings and propellors of the machine. If this ice is not melted or broken off by the use of special devices it may endanger the aircraft.

In a very heavy fall of rain from a thunder-cloud (what is called a cloud-burst) as much as $1\frac{1}{2}$ inches of water can fall in a very short time over an area of at least one square mile. This water would weigh over a hundred thousand tons. To support it in the air requires the upward-moving winds in the cloud to reach very considerable speeds over a large part of the cross-section of the cloud.

What conditions are like inside a thunder-cloud can best be described by those who have flown through one. Balloonists and airmen tell of extremely violent, gusty, and turbulent currents of air in which rain, snow, and hail seemed to bombard them from every angle. The commander of a German Zeppelin airship which was forced to enter a thunder-cloud during the First World War described his craft as behaving like a cork in a very heavy sea. At one moment it was forced down to 600 feet above ground and at another it was carried up to 6,000 feet, with St. Elmo's Fire streaming from every point of the ship. The British airship R. 100, which entered a thunder-cloud between Quebec and Montreal at the end of its transatlantic journey to Canada in 1930, experienced violent vertical gusts which carried it upwards at 50 miles an hour from 1,200 to 4,500 feet as if it were in a fast passenger lift. At 4,500 feet the airship ceased to rise any more and came under control again in a deluge of rain.

In the course of extensive thunderstorm investigations recently carried out in the United States and mentioned in Chapter 5, p. 50, it has been possible to measure the up and down speeds of air-currents in a number of clouds. The up-draught has been found to vary from a few feet per second, about 2 miles an hour, in the early stages of development of a thunder-cloud, to 100 feet per second, nearly 70 miles an hour, in the large well-developed cells which make up a powerful storm.

Hailstones

That the updraughts in a thunder-cloud are indeed very powerful is shown by the weight of the hailstones which they support. Hailstones are not solid ice through and through; when cut open with a saw they are found to be made up of concentric layers of ice and snow, showing that they have been bobbing up and down between the region of snow and that of water inside the cloud, at one time falling and collecting a layer of water and at another rising and so freezing the water to ice and collecting a coating of snow. The size to which hailstones can grow depends only on whether the upward winds are powerful enough to prevent them falling out of the cloud when they get too big.

The largest hailstones of whose size there is no possible doubt—like fishermen's catches, there have been reports of still larger ones—fell at a place called Potter, in Western Nebraska, in the year 1928. They were roughly round and were about the size of a large grapefruit, with an average diameter of $5\frac{1}{2}$ inches. The biggest weighed $1\frac{1}{2}$ pounds. A hailstone this size would fall through the air at a speed of 260 miles an hour and would be a very formidable missile. On this occasion, therefore, upward gusts reaching a speed of 260 miles an hour must have been blowing within the cloud.

But this was an exceptional case; the usual diameter of large hailstones is two to three inches, the size described as a hen's or goose's egg, a tennis ball or a man's fist. These fall at speeds of from 60 to 90 miles an hour, and their not infrequent occurrence shows that many thunder-clouds are kept up by vertical winds which at times and in places can reach at least 60 miles an hour. This agrees well with the measurements of the preceding section. The Potter hailstones were exceptional, because after a spherical hailstone reaches a diameter of 4·8 inches the air velocity needed to prevent it from falling out of the cloud jumps suddenly from 120 to 260 miles an hour, owing to a rapid alteration in the frictional resistance of the air when the motion of the boundary layer changes from streamline flow to turbulence.

The Source of Energy in the Thunder-cloud

Anyone who watches the chimney-pots and smoke-stacks of of a large city over which a thunder-cloud is forming will see from the drift of the smoke that the surface air is converging towards the cloud from all directions, and will deduce that it must be moving upwards into the cloud through its base. Under thunder-cloud conditions the warm air at the surface of the earth is very unstable and tends to rise upwards like a bubble in water. The cloud is a form of chimney in which this buoyant air can rise much more easily than anywhere else. In rising it passes into regions of lower pressure, and so expands. In expansion it cools, and so it gets colder and colder as it rises. The necessary condition for it to continue rising is that it should be warmer than the air it displaces.

At some stage it cools to the dew-point and begins to deposit the moisture in it as droplets of water. This stage is reached at the base of the cloud. How much farther it rises depends upon its original temperature and humidity and upon the state of the air it displaces.

It would, however, be wrong to suppose that this buoyancy of the warm surface air is the sole source of the energy responsible for the powerful updraughts in the thunder-cloud. Further energy comes to the uprising air from the act of depositing water, which gives back to the air the latent heat of condensation and consequently warms it. In a thunder-cloud the warmth so imparted to the uprising air is sufficient to keep it lighter than the air it displaces, in spite of the further cooling due to expansion as it rises. Thus the updraught climbs higher and higher until it has reached the stratosphere at about 35,000 feet, where the surrounding air no longer falls in temperature with height. (In the tropics this usually occurs at 50,000 feet.)

The developing thunder-cloud is, therefore, a great chimney-stack in which the air is given additional heat as it rises. In its later stages, as we shall see, it becomes a more complex affair. The falling out of rain and hail causes downdraughts to appear, and the single chimney-stack becomes a number of chimney-stacks as the cloud divides into cells.

The Mechanism of Electrification

It is at first sight somewhat strange that these great electrical machines, capable of developing potentials of thousands of millions of volts and of producing sparks many miles long, are made up of nothing but water and ice blown by the wind. But the effectiveness of the thunder-cloud as an electric generator arises from the enormous number of drops and ice-particles in it; though each of them is very feebly charged with electricity, their number is so great as to make up a considerable quantity of electric charge. To illustrate this point let us forget about hailstones and suppose that the cloud is composed entirely of water drops and ice particles of the size of the usual raindrop, that is, of diameter one-eighth of an inch (0·3 cms.). In a cloud containing 100,000 tons of water there would be six million million drops of this kind. Let us next suppose that each drop or ice particle carries a charge equal to that found by measurements at the ground to be about the average charge on a raindrop. This is one thirty thousand millionth part of a coulomb, and by multiplying the number of drops by the charge on each we find that together all the drops in the cloud carry 200 coulombs. Compared with the quantities in use in ordinary applications of electricity this is still small, for a coulomb is the quantity of electricity which flows through a 100-watt electric lamp in a little more than two seconds, but it is quite enough to account for all the lightning from the thunder-cloud and for other less spectacular electrical effects as well. The energy in a lightning-flash arises from small quantities of electricity at very high tensions and lasts, as we have seen, only for a very short time.

We must next consider the origin of the small charges of electricity on the drops or ice crystals. The difficulty here is not to discover a suitable mechanism but to determine which of a number of possible ways in which they can be charged is the one which plays the leading part in the thunder-cloud. To this question there is at present no final answer, only a number of interesting alternatives, the working out of which by theory and experiment has received, and is still receiving, the attention of many scientific workers. The reader must therefore be warned against accepting the explanations which follow as final; they should be preceded by the sign: 'Danger—Men at Work'.

The observations mentioned on p. 85 show that the large drops at the base of the cloud are charged with negative electricity. There are at least three possible ways in which this can happen. The first and simplest is the fact that all water drops, when they are first formed, have an attraction for negative ions in the air around them; this is a property arising from the electrical structure of the molecules of water in the drop. As soon as a droplet is formed by the condensation of water-vapour it becomes negatively charged by robbing its surroundings of a few negative ions and leaving an excess of positive ions in the neighbouring air. This is the theory of Frenkel.

The second explanation is that when particles of ice rub against each other they become negatively electrified by friction; the ice particles fairly high up in the cloud must thus be negatively charged, and the surrounding air must again carry an excess of positive charge in the form of ions or of tiny droplets or fragments of ice crystals. As the larger ice particles fall downwards they will melt to raindrops and give rise to the negatively charged drops which are observed, leaving positive charge higher up in the cloud. This is the theory of Simpson.

It is not yet clear whether either or both these two mechanisms is sufficient to create the amount of electricity found in thunder-clouds. They certainly operate, but it may well be that they themselves are only the initial 'primers' of a third one, which is much more effective than either of them. The third mechanism operates as follows: if, as a result of the two previous processes, there is already a positive charge in the upper part of the cloud and a negative charge below, any ice particle or water drop between the two will, as illustrated in Fig. 25, have an induced negative charge on its upper half and an induced positive (polarization) charge on its lower half. Whether such a drop is falling downwards, or is floating on the upward air-currents, or is being blown upwards, the air will be streaming past it carrying positive and negative ions.

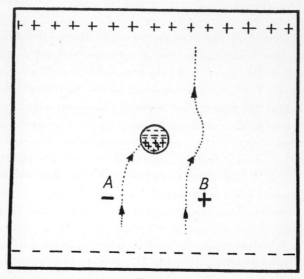

FIG. 25

A negative ion in the upward-moving air-stream, such as that shown at *A*, will tend to be pulled in to the drop by the attraction of the positive charge on the bottom of the drop. A positive ion, as at *B*, will be repelled by the positive charge on the bottom of the drop, and though later attracted by the negative charge on the top will not usually be able to get to it before it is swept away in the air-stream. The drop can in this way rob the air of large numbers of negative ions and acquire a net negative charge, while the upward-moving wind passes on with an excess of positive charge.

This third process has been suggested and worked out in detail by C. T. R. Wilson, and has been shown by laboratory experiments to work in the manner described. It is most effective when the air contains large numbers of negative and positive ions of a type which move slowly, and is for this reason likely to be operating most effectively when some other process, either or both of the first two which have been mentioned, has started the electrification of the cloud, and a certain amount of point discharge of ions from drops and ice particles has begun inside the cloud.

All three of these processes are possibly at work at one and the same time. All have the same result, for each leads to the appearance of negatively charged drops at the bottom of the cloud and an excess of positively charged ions on the uprising air. As they move upwards, most of the positive ions will attach themselves to tiny droplets and ice crystals and so charge the top of the cloud positively. In this way the upper and lower poles of the thunder-cloud are formed. In between them will be a region a mile or more in vertical extent in which the negatively charged larger and heavier drops and ice particles and the positively charged smaller droplets, snow and ice fragments, and the excess positive ions (the one group going down and the other going up) exist together and carry about equal quantities of electricity of opposite sign—a neutral region with no appreciable excess charge of either sign.

The separation of the charges in the thunder-cloud is thus brought about by the action of the wind in the same way as a winnowing-machine separates the light chaff (in this case the light positively charged droplets and ice fragments) from the heavier wheat (in this case the heavier negatively charged water drops and hailstones). To do this against their electrical attraction requires the performance of mechanical work, and it is this work, done by the wind, which accounts for the great electrical energy of the cloud and the existence between the poles of great potential differences, which are anything from a hundred million to a thousand million volts.

Once the charges on the cloud poles have been removed by a lightning-flash, the opposite charges in the intermediate neutral region continue the process of separating themselves out; fresh positively charged droplets and ions move upwards and fresh negatively charged raindrops and ice particles fall towards the base. The electric charges on the poles are renewed, the electric field recovers, and the stage is set for a fresh discharge. The rate of recovery of the field is at first very fast (if it continued to be as rapid, there would be another flash in five seconds) but slows down as the new charges develop. Their growth causes strong attractive forces to appear which resist the force of gravity, and also involves losses due to point discharge and similar processes.

Before leaving the subject of the origin of the electricity in a thunder-cloud, mention must be made of another mechanism by which drops can be electrified, but in an opposite manner to that just described. This is a process which occurs when a large drop is broken up into smaller ones because it has grown too big to be stable as it flattens out in its fall through the air. This process, which has been studied by Simpson and Lenard, leaves the fragments of the drop with a positive charge and the air with a negative one, so that it should act in the opposite manner to the three previously described, and should make the top of the cloud negative and the bottom positive.

Not so very long ago it was thought that the breaking-drop process played a predominant part in the electrification of thunder-clouds, but it has now become clear that the conditions for it to operate do not exist except in limited regions of the cloud, where very large water drops are held up by strong winds. Wherever it does take place it will act in the reverse manner to the three processes already described, creating a pocket of positively charged drops and leaving a negative charge on the upward-moving air. In this way it would act as a brake on the 'normal' development of the electrification of the cloud by the other processes; it is possible that its interaction with them is more complex, and that in some places it may help them and in others it may hinder them.

The reader will see that the explanation of what causes the electrification of thunder-clouds is at an interesting stage of experiment and argument, and that no finality has been reached. Four processes, which are certainly involved to a greater or lesser degree, have been discussed above, and there is still another possibility, as yet not fully examined, that the electricity is produced when water freezes to ice and snow in the colder upper portions of the cloud.

An Additional Method of Support: Electrical Attraction

It is possible that besides the direct action of the upward-moving winds on the drops in the base of a thunder-cloud, the electrical attraction between the charges at the top and the bottom of the cloud may play an important part in the process of supporting it in the air. The updraughts will have little difficulty in keeping the top portion of the cloud from falling, for this portion is composed of small droplets of super-cooled water and of tiny snowflakes, which fall so slowly that a vertical wind of a few miles an hour can hold them up. They are positively charged, while the raindrops in the base are negatively charged, so that if the updraught at the top of the cloud can enable the droplets there to carry the dead weight of the cloud as a whole, the attraction between them will prevent the heavy base from falling, without calling for direct support of the base by the winds. The additional mechanism of support is very similar to that provided by a parachute, which not only can reduce the rate of fall of a heavy weight to a very small value but can even pull it upwards if there is a strong upward breeze blowing. The strings of the 'parachute', as illustrated in Fig. 26, are the electrical attractions between the oppositely charged parts of the cloud.

It is a familiar experience to all who live in thundery regions that rain does not usually fall from a thunder-cloud until at least one lightning-flash has taken place. This may be due in part to the fact that the formation of large ice particles and drops is essential to the production of electricity by the cloud, but it seems possible that it arises from the action of the lightning-flash in causing the 'parachute' method of support to fail. With the passage of a flash within the cloud the electric charges momentarily disappear (the parachute-strings are broken) and the rain in the lower part of the cloud is free to fall. Often it does not get very far before the charges on the cloud are regenerated and the base of the cloud is held up once more by the restoration of the electric field.

As this may appear a very indirect argument, it is perhaps worth while quoting two others in support of it. The first is that calculation shows that the electrical attractions between

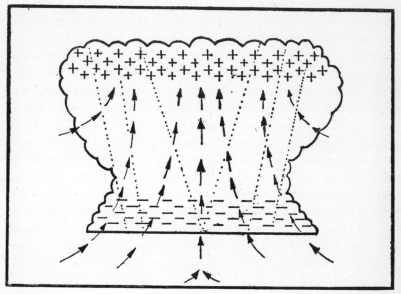

FIG. 26

the upper and lower charges are quite sufficient to carry the weight of the heavy base of the cloud. The second is that any experienced observer of lightning looks for it to appear not from the ragged edges of the cloud-base from which rain is falling, but from the taut, flat, black edge which can be pictured as held up by the invisible force of electrical attraction inside.

The reader may wonder how it is that rain ever escapes from such a cloud. Probably the major factor is the neutralization of the electricity on the drops in the under portion of the base by positive ions created from point discharge at the surface of the earth, as described earlier on p. 17. This positive 'space-charge' in the air below the cloud plays other parts. Its action in discharging the cloud-base is a constant drain on the electrical generating mechanism and can sometimes prevent the cloud from ever reaching the lightning-discharge state; though electrified, it is then a shower-cloud and not a thunder-cloud. The existence of space-charge in the air is also responsible for much of the extensive branching which is seen on flashes to ground, particularly over wooded country. It is quite possibly the most frequent means by which a lightning-flash to ground is triggered off, the initial stages of the pilot streamer leader-process being brought about by the presence of a strong concentration of positive ions in the air just below a strong concentration of negative charge on the cloud-base.

Rain-making: Natural and Artificial

The general conditions necessary for the development of a thunder-cloud have already been described. When these conditions are fulfilled, one or more cumulus clouds, containing only minute water droplets, are converted into a cumulo-nimbus cloud filled with large drops, snow, and hail. The change is often quite quick, and the manner in which it comes about was for a long time an unsolved meteorological problem, until in 1933 the Norwegian, Bergeron, put forward an explanation which goes a long way towards supplying the answer. This is the simple but revolutionary idea that the presence of ice crystals in a cloud is an essential preliminary to the formation of all rain. Though it is not accepted that Bergeron's hypothesis applies to all rain-clouds, it is probably true of most.

The minute droplets which make up ordinary clouds cannot, it is generally agreed, grow any larger by the condensation of water upon them; on the contrary, they tend to evaporate again even in saturated air. Nor is there much possibility that they can grow larger by joining forces and fusing together to form one drop out of many droplets. If, however, they are in a high portion of the cloud, where the temperature of the air is low enough for them to freeze to ice particles, it can be shown from elementary physics that these ice particles can at once grow much larger by drawing water from the air and from neighbouring unfrozen water droplets. As they increase in size they will fall slowly downwards, growing larger all the time, until they approach the bottom of the cloud, where the temperature is higher, when they begin to melt and turn into large water drops. If the winds are strong and gusty, these drops will have a long career of movement up and down in the cloud, and become hailstones.

It is, however, difficult for the Bergeron process to happen in any cloud unless it reaches to great heights. The droplets in a cumulus cloud, even when at a height where the temperature is many degrees below the freezing-point, obstinately refuse to freeze. They remain 'super-cooled' water droplets until they have been carried still higher, to a temperature which may, in the absence of special nuclei, be as low as 39° Centigrade below the freezing-point. Once they have got as high as this they have to freeze, and the stage is set for the major change from cumulus to cumulo-nimbus.

The freezing of the water droplets has another important effect on the cloud, for this process, like their original deposition from the air, gives out latent heat and warms the air, causing it to rise still higher into still cooler regions. In this way the first few droplets which freeze can start a trigger action which pushes the cumulus heads several thousand feet higher and changes the whole nature of the contents of the cloud, provided the upward winds are there to support the process and the general state of the air is such as to keep it going.

This, in brief, is what is now generally considered to be the natural way in which a cumulo-nimbus cloud forms from a cumulus cloud. It is to Irving Langmuir and his associates in the United States that we owe the development of the idea that if Nature depends upon a trigger—the freezing of super-cooled droplets—to form a rain-cloud, the trigger action might be started artificially. One method of doing this is to 'seed' the tops of cumulus clouds with small pellets of solid carbon dioxide (dry ice) dropped from an aircraft. These pellets have a surface temperature of 65° Centigrade below freezing-point, and as they fall they cool a thin streak of air in the cloud below the critical temperature for ice formation, producing millions of ice crystals which can grow to larger sizes without hindrance. Tests of this and similar methods of triggering have produced spectacular changes in cumulus clouds in the United States, Australia, and South Africa; in a few minutes the heads which have been seeded shoot high above the others and the clouds become charged with rain and ice.

The best way in which to tell whether the artificial triggering process has worked is to watch the cloud before and after seeding by means of a micro-wave radar set. The droplets in the original cumulus give no echoes back (on 3 cms. wave-length) to such a set, but if the cloud has changed to large drops and ice particles a strong echo is received. Used in this way in the summer of 1947–8 in South Africa, a radar set showed that out of 28 seeded cumulus clouds, 24 responded definitely to seeding. How far and in what way artificial rain-making will prove of practical value cannot be answered until more experimental work has been done. It remains to be seen whether in most cases when clouds are seeded the rain produced is of more than short duration. Even if it is not, the artificial stimulation of rain is likely to be of value in causing it to fall from clouds which would otherwise build up into destructive hailstorms.

The Development of the Thunderstorm

Four stages in the development of a tropical thunderstorm are depicted in Fig. 27. At A, on the left, is a cumulus cloud whose top extends to a height of about 20,000 feet, well above the freezing-level (0° C.), but does not reach to −39° Centigrade. This cloud everywhere consists of water droplets, those above the 0° Centigrade level being super-cooled.

At B, the cloud-top has shot up to a height of 35,000 feet (7 miles) and passed the critical −39° Centigrade level. Now many of the super-cooled droplets in its head have frozen to tiny ice crystals and formed soft hail and granular snow. These grow rapidly in size as they begin to fall. At C, they have formed hail or melted to large raindrops and have begun to fall out of the cloud as heavy rain. In their descent they have

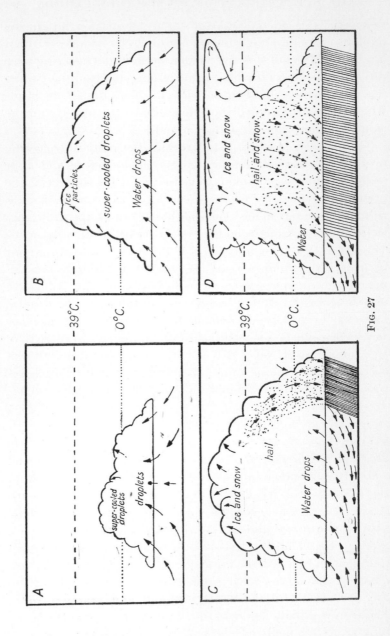

-39°C.

0°C.

A

super-cooled
droplets

droplets

B

ice
particles

super-cooled droplets

Water drops

-39°C.

0°C.

C

Ice and snow

hail

Water drops

D

Ice and snow

hail and snow

Water

FIG. 27

created a downdraught of cold air, as shown by the arrows, and this gust of cold down-coming air sweeps under the warm ascending air as a huge wedge, forcing it upwards and perpetuating the development of the storm. This is the mature stage of the storm, which may last for some hours.

The unshaded portion of the cloud in C, where the updraught continues to support the rain and hail and to drive positive charge upwards, is the centre of the electrical generating region which has been described in the previous pages. A large thunder-cloud may consist of a dozen such separate generating regions or cells, with rain and hail falling between them.

The electrical state and the electrical mechanism of the thunderstorm would be easier to discover if it were not for the downdraught regions shown in C. It is hard enough to study a natural phenomenon so difficult of access and so variable in its forms as a thunder-cloud; its habit of breaking into pieces by the falling out of hail and heavy rain produces an added complication. At the present time nothing is known with certainty as to the electrical conditions in the downdraught region.

The last drawing, D, of Fig. 27, shows the state of affairs in the final dissipating stage of the storm, which may be from one to three hours after it first began. The downdraught has spread across the lower levels of the cloud-cell to such an extent that the updraught has become of secondary importance. The top of the cloud has reached 50,000 feet (10 miles) and has spread out into an anvil because the temperature at that level no longer diminishes appreciably as the air rises upwards. Rain of moderate intensity falls from most of the base of the cloud, and the electrical activity, as shown by lightning-flashes, decreases until it stops altogether.

The four stages shown in Fig. 27 do not all occur at one place, for a cumulo-nimbus cloud travels in the direction of the upper air-current at a speed of from 15 to 35 miles an hour, renewing itself and obtaining further supplies of energy from the warm, water-charged air flowing into it from near the surface of the ground.

8

THE INDIRECT AND DISTANT EFFECTS OF THUNDERSTORMS

'That's enough about lessons', the Gryphon interrupted in
a very decided tone, 'tell her something about the games
now.'

Alice in Wonderland.

ONE of the deepest satisfactions in scientific work is the discovery and development of an intimate relation, such as a common cause or cause and effect, between two separate groups of known facts which had previously been thought to be unconnected. Franklin himself felt the 'exquisite pleasure' of this type of discovery when his experiments showed that thunder-clouds were electrical machines of the same general nature as the machine he had made in Philadelphia. The establishment of such a relationship between two groups of knowledge not only allows the facts in the one group to be explained and understood from a study of the other, but also leads to the really exciting business of finding new explanations of known facts and predicting phenomena yet to be discovered.

In this chapter an account is given of recent discoveries which relate lightning to two other fields of knowledge. The first of these fields is that of 'atmospherics' or 'static'—wireless-waves, most of which are now known to be lightning-waves from the thunderstorms of the world. The second is the continued electrification of the surface of the earth in fine weather, an electrification which has been an unsolved mystery for nearly two hundred years since its first discovery, but which has now been shown to be almost certainly due to the action of the world's thunderstorms.

Radio Atmospherics: Lightning-waves

Any very sudden change in the flow of an electric current produces what we know as a wireless-wave, a disturbance of the ether which spreads out from the source to give an effect which can be detected at a considerable distance from it. Sudden changes of this kind occur, as has been described in Chapters 4 and 5, at various stages in the progress of the electrical streamers which make up a lightning-flash, and the lightning-discharge is therefore capable of acting as a very powerful wireless-transmitter. The waves from a flash, though like other waves they diminish in strength with distance from their source, can be picked up on a wireless-receiver many thousands of miles away from the thunderstorm which produced them. They form a continuous background of crackling noise (called 'atmospherics' or 'static') on all except the very shortest wave-bands. This background noise is, in fact, the chief difficulty which has to be dealt with in maintaining wireless communications over long distances, because wireless messages, whether in speech or in morse code, must be louder than the noise-level of atmospherics at the receiver if they are to be intelligible.

The noise-level of atmospherics in any particular area is for this reason of great importance in the design and planning of radio-communication networks, particularly in tropical regions where, since thunderstorms are frequent and near, the noise-level is highest. During the recent World War a knowledge of the noise-level background in the Far East was urgently required in connexion with the establishment of military and naval wireless-communication systems in the Indian and Pacific Oceans. Since little was known of the noise-level a group of scientists was set to work to calculate it. For this they had the information which had been collected by meteorologists over the years about the world distribution and frequency of lightning-flashes, together with the newer information about the electrical processes occurring in lightning-discharges and the strength of atmospherics on various wave-bands at different distances from the parent flash. The results of their calculations were given to the Allied Forces in the form of world maps of atmospherics noise-level at different times of day and seasons of the year. These maps are proving extremely useful to-day in the planning of wireless communications and broadcasting, though the data in them are to some extent the results of very approximate calculations. A world-wide organization is at present at work obtaining direct measurements of noise-level with automatic recording instruments and making special studies of atmospherics and lightning-flashes. When the results of this work are available the planning of wireless communication and broadcasting systems in such areas as Africa and the Far East will be much less crude and approximate.

The Wave-form of Atmospherics

When examined with suitable instruments at a distance of about twenty miles from the flash which produced them, the wireless-waves from a discharge between cloud and ground have the general form shown in Fig. 28. They are recorded for purposes of study on the screen of a cathode-ray oscillograph tube, which fortunately retains the impression of their shape long after they have passed by at 186,000 miles a second. The atmospheric chosen for illustration came from a flash which consisted of two strokes. Some complications in the wave-form, which at fairly close distances are of only minor importance, have been omitted from the diagram. When atmospherics are examined in this way, some distance from the flash which caused them, the main waves are found to come from the only two really large and sudden electrical changes in the streamer-processes. These, as the reader will remember, are, firstly, the steps of the first leader-process and, secondly, the great rush of current in the return streamer of each stroke. The dart leaders are not sudden enough in their onset to produce waves of comparable size, and after they have started they move too smoothly down the channel to give rise to wireless-waves.

The wave-form begins with a long series of small ripples, marked A in the figure, each one of which corresponds to a single step in the first leader-process. The whole series of these ripples passes the observing point for as long as the first leader takes to reach the ground—usually about a hundredth of a second. As has been described on p. 82, each ripple lasts for from 30 to 90 micro-seconds and the average frequency of the ripples in the *A* portion is 20,000 cycles per second. These are the waves used to trigger the camera described in Chapter 4, so that a flash can take its own photograph.

When the last of the leader ripples has passed by, there arrives a single powerful wave, *B*, which is caused by the sudden starting up of the heavy-current return streamer. Its

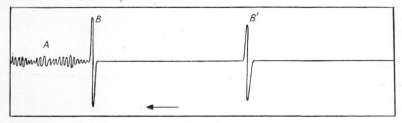

FIG. 28

duration is usually about 30 micro-seconds, which is the time taken for the sudden flow of current in the return stroke to establish itself.

After this there is a pause until the *B* wave from the return streamer of the second stroke of the same flash arrives. This, which is shown as *B'*, has no *A* series of waves preceding it, for its steadily moving dart leader does not involve large sudden changes of current.

Flashes within the cloud, and the air-discharges described on p. 79, give rise to rather complicated waves of the general form of the *A* series in Fig. 27; they show no *B* waves since they have no return-stroke processes associated with them.

Reflection of Lightning-waves from the Ionosphere

A remarkable change takes place in the appearance of these waves when they are examined at a greater distance from the flash which caused them to start. This is shown in Fig. 29, for an atmospheric which has travelled 200 miles; the ripples in the *A* portion have become more numerous and complex, and the *B* waves now show a series of repetitions of themselves at intervals which become longer and longer at each repetition. These are marked G and G', S_1, S_2, S_3, &c., in the figure.

The reason for this change is that waves are now reaching the observing equipment after travelling by different and longer paths. As shown in Fig. 30, the first set is that which has arrived directly as a 'ground-wave' and corresponds exactly to the waves of Fig. 28; its B portions are marked G in Fig. 29,

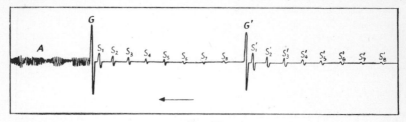

Fig. 29

and in Fig. 30 its path is the dotted line marked G. After the G waves there follow new sets of waves which are echoes sent back and forth between the reflecting layer about 60 miles above the earth (the layer which is called the ionosphere) and the ground. The first of these begins its career by travelling upwards, and is then turned downwards by one reflection from the ionosphere. This is appropriately called the first 'sky-wave', and marked S_1 in Fig. 29; its path is marked in Fig. 30 with the symbol 1.

Later follow sets of sky-waves which have undergone 2, 3, 4, and more reflections from the ionosphere and 1, 2, 3, and more reflections from the earth. Since the reflections are not perfect, the size of these later sky-waves is generally less than that of the direct ground-wave, and their form is smoothed out by successive reflecting processes and by imperfections in the reflecting quality of the ionosphere. Records of the form of Fig. 29 can, therefore, be obtained with the clarity shown in the diagram only if they are sought for during the night hours, when the lower edge of the ionosphere, as a result of the removal of the sun's rays, has contracted upwards and is reasonably sharp. As many as forty reflections have been observed at night; by day the number is seldom more than four. The same multiplicity of echoes occurs on the A portion of the wave-form, but it overlaps with the direct waves from successive leader steps in such a way as to make this part of the record too complicated to interpret.

From a study of the intervals of time between the arrivals of successive waves in the G and S series of Fig. 29 it is possible

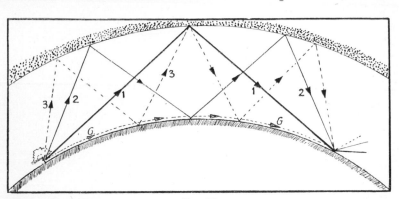

FIG. 30

to find the height of the reflecting layer responsible for these effects. It turns out to be 60 miles above the earth at night, but by day it is lower and the edge of its boundary is indeterminate.

A set of atmospheric wave-forms obtained from different flashes at various distances is shown in Fig. 31. The distance each had travelled from the flash which gave rise to it is marked in kilometres on the right-hand side. The A ripples have been omitted from the drawings.

One interesting feature of this diagram is that, as the *distance* between the parent flash and the recording-point increases, the sky-waves follow after the ground-wave and after one another at intervals of time which become progressively smaller. This is shown by the dotted lines joining the various S peaks. After the first four records, i.e., after about 720 kilometres, it is no longer possible to separate the

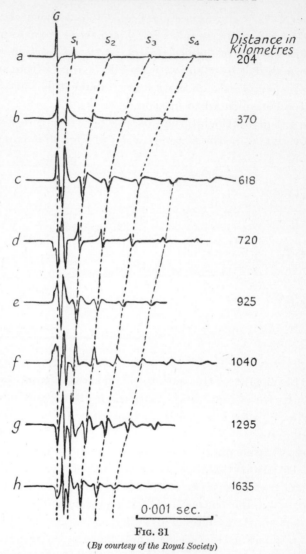

FIG. 31

(*By courtesy of the Royal Society*)

ground-wave and the first sky-wave from one another, because the interval between them is too small.

The reason for this change in the interval between the arrival of G and S_1, to take only one case, can be understood by reference to Fig. 30. When the distance is small, the S_1 path, which is marked 1, involves a turn-round of nearly 180° at the ionosphere and a considerably greater distance of travel than the direct G path. At great distances the angle is smaller and so is the difference in length between the two paths.

Another important feature of the wave-forms is that the interval between successive peaks (such as $G–S_1$, $S_1–S_2$, $S_2–S_3$, and so on) on the same atmospheric gets larger and larger as the number of the sky-wave rises. This is due to exactly the same cause; the higher the number of the sky-wave, the more its path approaches one in which its successive zigzags are vertical and longer than those of its predecessor. This difference in interval times is dependent upon the distance, and can be expressed in a simple formula relating the interval of time between any two sky-waves to the sky-wave numbers involved, the height of the reflecting layer, and the distance. By applying this formula to the intervals it is possible, as was first proposed by Laby and a group of Australian workers, to find both the distance of the originating flash and the height of the ionosphere, and this by making measurements on one single atmospheric wave-form. The author has found that the distances obtained in this way agree very closely with the known distances of thunderstorms, determined either from meteorological reports or by the direction-finding methods to be described on p. 142.

As has been said, the incidence of sky-waves upon the ionosphere becomes more and more nearly vertical as the number of hops involved in their path increases. As a consequence, the interval between one sky-wave and the next, though it increases with the number of the sky-wave, tends, in the case of high-numbered sky-waves with many hops, to reach a limit which is very near to the time taken by a wireless-wave in actually travelling vertically from the ground to the ionosphere and back again. This fact provides another method of measuring the height of the ionosphere layer concerned in the reflection of atmospherics.

Records g and h of Fig. 31 are particularly interesting; though the time intervals between their sky-waves are different, they show a strong family resemblance in detail because they arose from the same lightning-flash. This flash discharged into the sea from a thunder-cloud 400 miles south-east of Cape Town; record *g* shows the form of the atmospheric as received in Johannesburg, 1,295 km. away, and record *h* shows the form it took when it arrived, by a different path and a thousandth of a second later, in Durban, 1,635 km. away.

The Use of Atmospherics in Statistical Studies of the Distribution and Nature of Lightning-flashes

The examination of records of their wave-form offers a valuable method of studying and sampling large numbers of lightning-flashes. Since a single recording station can receive atmospherics from all storms within a radius of several thousand miles, a great deal of information can be got from studies of atmospherics about the way in which thunderstorm activity varies in different areas at different times and seasons. In addition, since the waves arise from sudden large changes in the current in various stages of the discharge-process, studies of wave-form can also be used to provide statistical information about these current changes. Those flashes which have passed between cloud and ground can readily be picked out from flashes within the cloud by the fact that they alone produce the *A* and *B* combination of waves shown in Figs. 27 and 28. A study of the *G* portions of atmospherics like that depicted in Fig. 28 can, for example, give the duration and the rate of rise and fall of the currents in the return strokes of flashes hundreds of miles away. It would take very many years to get observations on such a large number of flashes in any other way.

Locating Thunderstorms by Direction-finding of Atmospherics

A radio direction-finder in its simplest form involves a screened receiver which picks up the waves by means of an aerial consisting of a loop of wire. This aerial gives the loudest signal when turned in the direction of the transmitting station. With modern refinements a direction-finder can give the bearing of the source of the waves to within half a degree and can indicate it automatically on a dial. Two or, preferably, three such stations, when spaced at a suitable distance from one another, are used to locate the position of the transmitting station on a map by the intersection of their bearing lines. The method can be employed to locate thunderstorms, or rather lightning-flashes from them, by determining the directions of arrival of atmospherics. Equipment developed by Watson-Watt for this purpose has been widely used, especially in war-time, to find the positions of distant storms when these storms are taking place over inaccessible territory or over the oceans.

The direction of arrival of a 'lightning-wave' is shown by a bright line on the face of a cathode-ray tube carrying a super-imposed compass scale. Although the atmospheric itself has a very short duration, the tube afterglow enables the observer to make an accurate reading. The receivers operate on a fre-quency of 12·5 kcs./sec., this being the frequency at which the maximum energy will be picked up, since it covers the series of waves of Fig. 28 fairly well. The meteorological information obtained by this system, which goes by the unfortunate name of 'sferics', is of value not only in connexion with aircraft flights but also for general forecasting purposes. In Great Britain the Meteorological Office maintains four such stations, each with a range of 1,500 miles, at Dunstable, Camborne, Leuchars in Fife, and Irvinestown in Northern Ireland. Observations are made simultaneously from all four stations twelve times daily. The results of their readings, after plotting at Dunstable, are broadcast by teleprinter and by wireless, enabling pilots of aircraft to avoid storm areas and thus reduce the risk of accidents.

Two good examples of the reliability of this method of locating thunderstorms, which has an accuracy of 30 miles at 600 miles distance, are shown in Fig. 32.

To obtain this information two automatic direction-finding stations were set up in 1938 in Johannesburg and Durban, 300 miles apart, marked J and D on each map. These were connected together by telephone, and observers recorded the bearings of sources of atmospherics for a quarter of an hour each day round about 1 p.m. The remarkable results of this quick look at the thunderstorm situation are shown by the intersections of the bearings taken when compared with the crosses, which show all the storms reported over the land during the whole day by the meteorological service. These are, of course, two specially simple cases of days of few storms, but on most days, unless there were too many storms, the results were

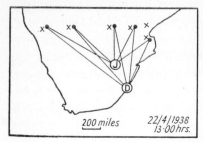 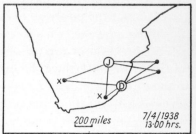

FIG. 32

nearly as good. The system is clearly of great value to meteorological forecasting organizations, though to maintain two or three direction-finding stations with telephone links between them costs a good deal. For this reason workers in various countries are now experimenting with a view to combining a single atmospheric direction-finding station of this kind, giving a single bearing, with a recorder of wave-form which, as described on p. 141, will give the distance of the source directly. This combination of bearing and distance should make it possible to locate thunderstorms from one station only and so to dispense with the costly telephone links at present required.

Lightning-alarms and Counting Devices

There are to-day a number of industrial enterprises which, in spite of the installation of protective equipment and lightning-rods, are still anxious when thunderstorms are about. Chief amongst these are factories in which explosives are manufactured, the modern counterparts of the powder magazines which suffered so much from lightning in the earlier days, described in Chapter 1. Others are electric power companies whose service, as described on p. 114, may be interrupted by a stroke, and mining undertakings which sink shafts with the aid of electrically fired charges of dynamite. A number of fatal accidents have been caused by the connexion of the detonators of such charges to the surface when thunderstorms capable of inducing electrical currents in the wires were in the neighbourhood. To this list of the people interested in timely warning of storms may be added those who man captive barrage-balloons in war-time (p. 112).

A general warning of storms can be provided by modifying a simple form of radio-receiver to ring a bell when atmospherics of an amplitude which indicates that the parent storm is near are received. By turning a switch to make the instrument less sensitive, it can then be set to give a more 'imminent' alarm. The weakness of such devices is that they do not give a warning within very close limits of distance nor do they tell the route the storm is taking. If this information is required the only solution is to use a micro-wave radar set which shows, by the echo received from it, the position of a thunderstorm on a map just as it shows the position of aircraft.

Another device, recently developed in South Africa, and called a ceraunometer (from the Greek ceraunos, a lightning-flash), performs the functions of a lightning alarm but operates within closer limits of distance than the simple radio-receiver. It can be arranged to give a fairly definite warning of flashes within a distance of twenty miles and another of flashes within seven miles. It can be adapted to record these flashes on counters, and from these records the number of lightning-flashes to ground per square mile per year can be calculated. This information is of value to electric power companies which are planning developments in new areas where lightning is prevalent.

The Charging of the Earth

The maintenance and the nature of the permanent electric charge on the surface of the earth is the second of the two fields of knowledge which, as mentioned earlier in this chapter, have been linked with the study of thunderstorms.

St. Elmo's Fire is a powerful visible form of point discharge, accompanied by light and a crackling sound. A less obvious, because invisible and silent, form of discharge is taking place all the time a thunder-cloud is active above the earth. Each projecting point, bush or tree, or building is silently discharging electricity upwards in the form of ions, like the earthed rod illustrated in Fig. 2. Though the current from any one point is very small, the whole effect from all is considerable. Some years ago the writer cut down a small thorn-tree, typical of those in the country-side in which he lived, and mounted it on insulators as in Fig. 33. (The drawing is not to scale.) Measurements were made of the current passed upwards during thunderstorms when the tree was connected to earth through a micro-ammeter at A. When it was not so connected it charged up like Franklin's rod in Fig. 1 and gave most unpleasant sparks if touched by the hand. On multiplying the average current through the tree at various distances from the storm by the number of trees of the same kind which would be similarly affected at any particular moment, and adding the results, it was found that the total current passing upwards from projecting trees was at least three amperes. This is a current of the same magnitude as that developed by the thunder-cloud in between its poles. Regarded as an electric generator, then, the cloud is connected to an external circuit which, as shown in Fig. 33, involves the earth and the upper air. The same process must be taking place underneath all thunder-clouds, and as the great majority of them have negatively charged bases, the total effect is to draw a considerable positive charge from the earth and so to leave a considerable negative charge on it, in addition to that conveyed to it by lightning flashes. There is, however, a counteracting process to be considered; most raindrops carry down a positive charge when they strike the ground. At first sight this appears to be in contradiction to what has been found about their charge when in the cloud, but in fact the drops as they fall to earth meet such a concentration of positive ions due to point discharge that their original negative charge is neutralized and reversed by the Wilson process described on p. 124. The charge on rain thus returns some, but not all, of the positive charge drawn from the earth by the silent point discharge. Long-continued

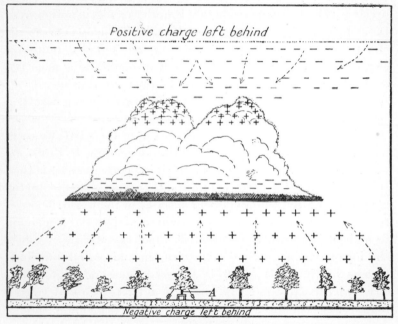

Positive charge left behind

Negative charge left behind

FIG. 33

observations carried out by Wormell in England indicate that on balance the earth is in all probability negatively charged by thunderstorms and rain-showers. Recent measurements in aircraft above thunder-clouds have shown that currents from the tops of the clouds to the upper air charge the upper air positively in a similar manner, drawing negative ions out of it and leaving a net positive charge behind.

These charges on earth and upper air spread quickly over both surfaces and show themselves all over the world in fine-weather regions. Their existence has been known for over a hundred years, but until recently no acceptable explanation could be offered for them. For unless there were some charging process *continually* at work, the ordinary feeble electrical conductivity of the air would be sufficient to pass a current in the fine-weather areas of the earth which would enable the two sets of charges to neutralize each other in about ten minutes. It would seem that thunderstorms offer the solution to the mystery; there are about 44,000 thunder-clouds in action over the whole world every day and each of these acts as an electrical generator floating between earth and sky, pumping electricity from one to the other, and so maintaining negative and positive charges on earth and upper air respectively in spite of the contrary leakage current flowing in fine-weather regions.

This explanation of the electrification of the earth we owe, like much else of modern work on thunderstorms, to Professor C. T. R. Wilson. One of its rather striking consequences is that the charge upon the earth in fine-weather regions should fluctuate with the total thunderstorm activity of the world. Though this activity is likely to be very variable and irregular from hour to hour, it is known to be greatest when the afternoon sun is shining on Africa and South America, the main equatorial landmasses of the earth, that is between one and eight p.m. Greenwich mean time. The smallest activity is about twelve hours later. On the average, then, the earth's charge should reach its maximum and minimum values at these same times. This prediction has been brilliantly fulfilled by observation; in fact, a daily variation of the earth's charge of exactly this nature was discovered many years before Wilson's suggestion, as a result of observations of the earth's charge made on the voyages of the American scientific research ship *Carnegie* and during expeditions to the Arctic and Antarctic. The variation has had to be established by such measurements over the sea and the earth's ice-caps since smoke and dust on ordinary land produce local changes which confuse the issue.

INDEX

PRINTED IN GREAT BRITAIN
AT THE UNIVERSITY PRESS, OXFORD
BY CHARLES BATEY, PRINTER TO THE UNIVERSITY